GCSE 9–1
PHYSICS
EXAM PRACTICE
FOR ALL EXAM BOARDS

Sam Jordan

Author Sam Jordan
Editorial team Haremi Ltd
Series designers emc design ltd
Typesetting York Publishing Solutions Pvt. Ltd., INDIA
Illustrations York Publishing Solutions Pvt. Ltd., INDIA
App development Hannah Barnett, Phil Crothers and Haremi Ltd

Designed using Adobe InDesign
Published by Scholastic Education, an imprint of Scholastic Ltd, Book End, Range Road, Witney,
Oxfordshire, OX29 0YD
Registered office: Westfield Road, Southam, Warwickshire CV47 0RA
www.scholastic.co.uk

Printed by Bell & Bain Ltd, Glasgow
© 2017 Scholastic Ltd
1 2 3 4 5 6 7 8 9 7 8 9 0 1 2 3 4 5 6

British Library Cataloguing-in-Publication Data
A catalogue record for this book is available from the British Library.
ISBN 978-1407-17690-1

Acknowledgements

Every effort has been made to trace copyright holders for the works reproduced in this book, and the publishers apologise for
any inadvertent omissions.

Note from the publisher:

Please use this product in conjunction with the official specification that you are following and sample assessment materials for
the exam board that will be setting your examinations. Ask your teacher if you are unsure where to find them. Mapping grids
showing you which content you need to know for the main specifications are found online at www.scholastic.co.uk/gcse.

The marks and star ratings have been suggested by our subject experts, but they are to be used as a guide only.

Answer space has been provided, but you may need to use additional paper for your workings.

Contents

Contents

How to use this book

This Exam Practice Book has been produced to help you revise for your 9–1 GCSE in physics. Written by an expert and packed full of exam-style questions for each subtopic, along with full practice papers, it will get you exam ready!

The best way to retain information is to take an active approach to revision. Don't just read the information you need to remember – do something with it! Transforming information from one form into another and applying your knowledge will ensure that it really sinks in. Throughout this book you'll find lots of features that will make your revision practice an active, successful process.

EXAM-STYLE QUESTIONS

Exam-style questions for each subtopic ramped in difficulty.

For mapping grids to show you exactly what you need to know for your specification and tier, go to www.scholastic.co.uk/gcse

DOIT!

Tasks that support your understanding and analysis of a question.

WORKIT!

Worked examples with model solutions to help you see how to answer a tricky question.

Callouts Step-by-step guidance to build understanding.

NAILIT!

Tips to help you perform in the exam.

★ STAR RATING ★

A quick visual guide to indicate the difficulty of the question, with 1 star representing the least demanding and 5 stars signposting the most challenging questions.

MARKS (5 marks)

Each question has the number of marks available to help you target your response.

STRETCHIT!

Questions or concepts that stretch you further and challenge you with the most difficult content.

PRACTICE PAPERS

Full mock-exam papers to enable you to have a go at a complete paper before you sit the real thing!

For an additional practice paper, visit: www.scholastic.co.uk/gcse

Use the Physics Revision Guide for All Boards alongside the Exam Practice Book for a complete revision and practice solution. Written by a subject expert to match the new specifications, the Revision Guide uses an active approach to revise all the content you need to know!

HOW TO REVISE!

PLAN YOUR REVISION

Get ahead by planning your revision!

Work out the **time** you have available for revising.

Think about when you work at your best. Are you a morning or an evening person?

Allocate **MORE TIME** for the topics you struggle with.

Revision works best in **SMALL BURSTS**, so keep sessions **SHORT AND SWEET**!

Remember to allow time to **PRACTISE** applying what you have revised.

Use your **revision app** to put together a revision timetable.

LOOK AFTER YOURSELF

Help your brain by looking after your whole body!

Take regular **breaks** from revising – your brain needs time to digest information in order to retain it.

HOTEL

Keep **hydrated** by drinking plenty of water – dehydration stops your brain from working at its full capacity.

Regular **exercise** helps stimulate the brain and will help you relax.

Get plenty of **sleep**, especially the night before an exam.

EAT WELL and limit unhealthy snacks – your brain needs fuel for memory and concentration.

Find methods of **relaxation** that work for you throughout the revision period.

BE PREPARED!

Limit potential stress on the day of an exam by getting everything you need ready the night before.

30

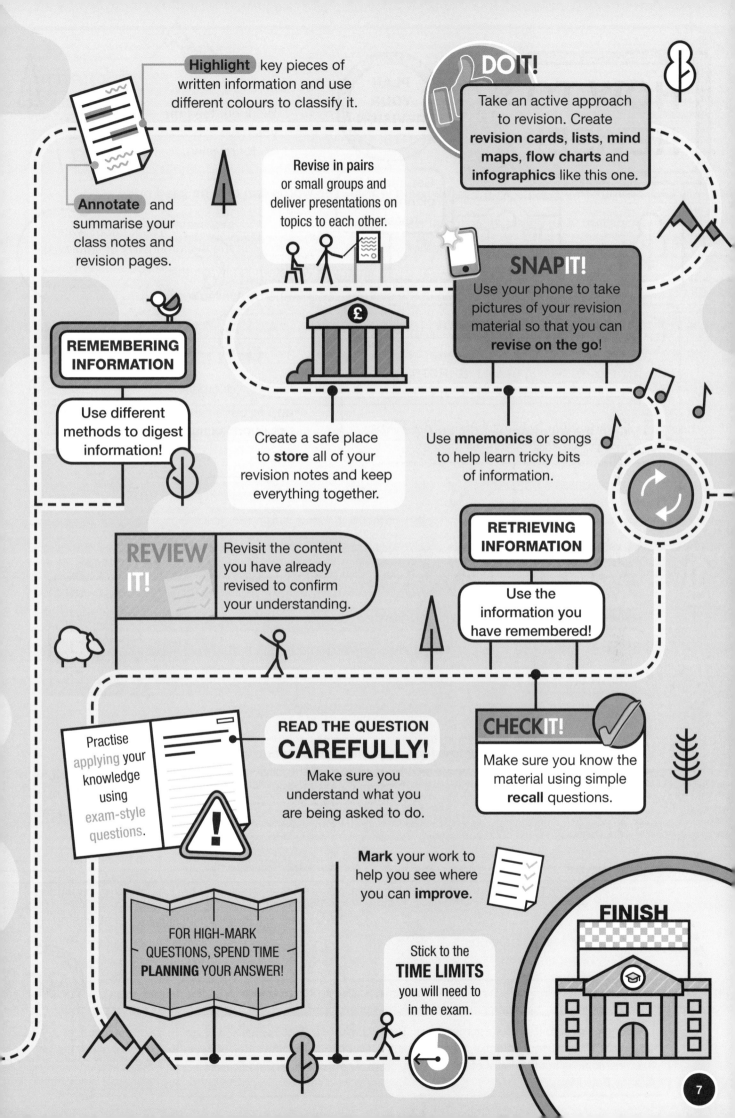

Highlight key pieces of written information and use different colours to classify it.

Annotate and summarise your class notes and revision pages.

DO IT!
Take an active approach to revision. Create **revision cards, lists, mind maps, flow charts** and **infographics** like this one.

Revise in pairs or small groups and deliver presentations on topics to each other.

SNAP IT!
Use your phone to take pictures of your revision material so that you can **revise on the go**!

REMEMBERING INFORMATION

Use different methods to digest information!

Create a safe place to **store** all of your revision notes and keep everything together.

Use **mnemonics** or songs to help learn tricky bits of information.

RETRIEVING INFORMATION

Use the information you have remembered!

REVIEW IT!
Revisit the content you have already revised to confirm your understanding.

Practise *applying* your knowledge using *exam-style questions.*

READ THE QUESTION CAREFULLY!
Make sure you understand what you are being asked to do.

CHECK IT!
Make sure you know the material using simple **recall** questions.

Mark your work to help you see where you can **improve**.

FOR HIGH-MARK QUESTIONS, SPEND TIME **PLANNING** YOUR ANSWER!

Stick to the **TIME LIMITS** you will need to in the exam.

FINISH

Energy stores and systems

(1) Complete the gaps with the following words. The words can only be used once. (3 marks, ★★★)

A system is an object, or group of objects. The .... in a system is a numerical .... that tells us whether certain .... in the system could, or could not, happen. The total .... of energy in a system is always the .... no matter what changes happen in the system, but the energy available can be .... in different parts of this system.

amount	form	different	energy	changes
same	redistributed	kinetic	decreases	value

(2) Match the following energy stores to where they are found. Two have been done for you. (3 marks, ★★)

1 Gravitational potential	**a** Fuel
2 Kinetic	**b** A position in the gravitational field
3 Thermal	**c** In a stretched or compressed spring
4 Nuclear	**d** In a warm object
5 Magnetic	**e** In two separated magnets that attract/repel
6 Elastic potential	**f** In two separated charges that attract/repel
7 Electrostatic	**g** Large unstable nuclei such as plutonium and uranium
8 Chemical	**h** In a moving object

(3) Complete the flowchart below for someone making a cup of tea at a campsite with a saucepan and butane burner. (5 marks, ★★)

2 By ....

4 .... store

Hot water in pan

Butane and oxygen

Pan and air surrounding pan

1 .... store

3 By ....   5 .... store

DO IT!

Think about different situations and the changes in the energy stores that take place. Can you identify the useful energy stores or pathways? For example, a boy flicking an elastic band, a girl climbing up some stairs, or a sky diver on his descent.

NAILIT!

Use a mnemonic to learn the energy stores: **T**hermal, **N**uclear, **E**lectrostatic, **C**hemical, **G**ravitational potential, **E**lastic potential, **M**agnetic. The first letter of the mnemonic is the first letter of each energy store: **T**homas **N**ever **E**ats **C**arrots **G**ranny **E**ats **M**any.

Changes in energy stores: kinetic energy

(1) a **Write the equation used to calculate the kinetic energy of a moving object.** (1 mark, ★★)

....

b **Write the unit for the energy in a kinetic store.**
(1 mark, ★★)

....

(2) **A car of mass 1000 kg is moving at 10 m/s. Calculate the car's energy in the kinetic store.** (2 marks, ★★★)

....

....

WORKIT!

How to tackle a question where you would normally rearrange the equation at the beginning.

Calculate the speed of a 6000 kg bus with 3.7 MJ of energy in the kinetic store. (4 marks, ★★★)

Step 1 $E_k = 0.5 \times m \times v^2$ ⟵ ⟶ Write the formula but don't try to rearrange. Write 0.5 instead of $\frac{1}{2}$.

Step 2 Substitute in the values you are given.

$3\,700\,000 = 0.5 \times 6000 \times v^2$ (1) ⟵ ⟶ Leave v^2 alone!

Step 3 Multiply out right-hand terms 0.5 and 6000.

$3\,700\,000 = 3000 \times v^2$ (1) ⟵ ⟶ To get v^2 on its own divide both sides by 3000.

Step 4 $\dfrac{3\,700\,000}{3000} = \dfrac{3000}{3000} \times v^2$

Step 5 Swap v^2 to the left-hand side and take the square root of both sides.
Remember → $\sqrt{v^2} = v \rightarrow v = \sqrt{1233} = 35\,m/s$ (1)

The bus is going at 35 m/s which is approximately 70 mph. It should slow down! (1)

For those who are good at rearranging equations: $v = \sqrt{\dfrac{2 \times E_k}{m}} = \sqrt{\dfrac{2 \times 3\,700\,000}{3000}} = 35\,m/s$

(3) **A train is travelling at a speed of 10 m/s and has 0.8 MJ of energy in the kinetic store. Calculate the train's mass.** (4 marks, ★★★★)

....

....

....

....

NAILIT!

Don't forget that the unit of kinetic energy is joules or J. Remember that all of the energy stores and work done have the unit joules or J. It doesn't matter whether it is nuclear or chemical. Energy stores are always measured in joules or J.

Changes in energy stores: elastic potential energy

(1) **State the elastic potential energy equation.** (1 mark, ★★★)

....

....

(2) **A spring has a spring constant $k = 10\,N/m$.**

A force is applied to stretch the spring. The spring's length increases from 5 cm to 25 cm.

Calculate the energy in the elastic potential store of the spring. (4 marks, ★★★★)

Metre rule

Spring

Slotted mass

....

....

....

(3) **A force of 2.5 N is applied to a spring. The spring's length increases from 10 cm to 20 cm.**

Calculate the spring constant of the spring. Express your answer in N/m. (4 marks, ★★★)

....

....

....

....

(4) **A fisherman has a fish on the end of his rod, and is trying to reel it in.**

His fishing rod line has 20 J of energy in the elastic potential store. The spring constant of the line is 10 kN/m.

Calculate the extension of the line in cm. (4 marks, ★★★★★)

....

....

....

Changes in energy stores: gravitational potential energy

(1) **State the gravitational potential energy equation.** (1 mark, ★★★)

....

....

....

> **DO IT!**
>
> Memorise the gravitational potential energy equation. Write it out over and over again.

Use (g = 10 N/kg) for all questions.

(2) **Calculate the (energy) gain in the gravitational potential store of a power drill when a power drill of 4 kg is lifted upwards 4 m by a man climbing a ladder.** (2 marks, ★★★)

....

....

....

> **NAILIT!**
>
> Remember that weight is a force and
> weight = mass × gravitational field strength.
> Do you notice any similarity between the formula for work done and gravitational potential energy?

(3) **Calculate the (energy) gain in the gravitational potential store when a mass of 40 kg is lifted upwards 500 cm by a forklift.** (2 marks, ★★★)

....

....

....

(4) **Calculate the height fallen by a ball of mass 300 g if the energy in the gravitational store decreases by 90 J.** (4 marks, ★★★★)

....

....

....

....

Energy changes in systems: specific heat capacity

Specific heat capacities to be used in questions:

Water: 4200 J/kg °C   Ethanol: 2400 J/kg °C

Rubber: 2000 J/kg °C   Air: 1000 J/kg °C

Copper: 390 J/kg °C

(1) a Write a definition for specific heat capacity. (1 mark, ★★)

....

....

b State the equation for specific heat capacity. (1 mark, ★★)

....

c Write the unit for specific heat capacity. (1 mark, ★★)

....

(2) Two objects of the same mass are heated up on a hotplate for the same amount of time.

One is made of copper, the other of steel.

The copper object rises in temperature from 25°C to 35°C.

The temperature of the iron object increases only from 25°C to 30°C.

Using ideas about specific heat capacity, explain why this happens. (3 marks, ★★★★)

> **NAILIT!**
>
> Remember specific heat capacity is a measure of how much energy is required to raise the temperature of 1 kg of a substance by 1°C. Metals require less energy to change their temperature than non-metals. Use this to consider why metals feel colder than non-metals.

....

....

....

(3) A teacher uses a Bunsen burner to heat some ethanol in a beaker.

The energy supplied by the burner is 1.5 kJ.

The temperature increases from 25°C to 35°C.

Find the mass of ethanol in kg that was heated.
(4 marks, ★★★★)

> **DOIT!**
>
> Think about why a fruit pie feels quite cool on the outside but when you bite into the filling it burns your tongue. Try to explain why this happens. It has something to do with specific heat capacity.

....

....

....

....

Power

1. Bill and Ted went to the gym. They argued about who was the most powerful. They decided on three tests in the gym to see who was correct. First, they bench-pressed 30 kg for 60 seconds. Next they timed how many step-ups they could do in 60 seconds. Finally, they did kettle bell raises for 60 seconds. Their results are shown in the table.

Activity	Bill	Ted
Bench press	50 repetitions in 60 s Uses 7.5 kJ in total Power	42 repetitions in 60 s Uses 6.3 kJ in total Power ....
Step-ups	89 repetitions in 60 s Uses 17.8 kJ in total Power	100 repetitions in 60 s Uses 20 kJ in total Power ....
Kettle bell raises	60 raises in 60 s Uses 7.2 kJ in total Power	67 raises in 60 s Uses 8.04 kJ in total Power ....

power = energy transferred ÷ time

a **Calculate the power of each man for each activity and add to the table above.** (6 marks, ★★★)

b **Who was the most powerful overall?** (2 marks, ★★★)

....

(2) **A television has a power rating of 50 watts.**

It is switched on for $7\frac{1}{2}$ hours.

Calculate the energy transferred in this time. (2 marks, ★★★)

....

....

(3) **A forklift works at 100 kW of power.**

The forklift requires 2200 kJ of energy to lift a heavy crate onto a higher loading platform.

Calculate the time taken for the forklift to load the crate onto the platform. (3 marks, ★★★★)

....

....

....

DO IT!

Make an effort to learn what the different metric prefixes mean. They are used a lot in power and energy questions. Make sure you know:

1 kW = 1 kilowatt = 1000 watts and 1 MW = 1 megawatt = 1 000 000 watts.

If you are confident in the use of standard form then use the following notation: $1\,kW = 1 \times 10^3\,W$ and $1\,MW = 1 \times 10^6\,W$

Energy transfers in a system

(1) **State the conservation of energy law.** (2 marks, ★★★)

....

....

(2) **Look at the table.**

Complete the table by giving examples of devices where electricity can be transferred into each of the energy stores.

(3 marks, ★★★)

Electricity changes into:	Example
Gravitational potential store	
Vibrational store	
Thermal store	

(3) **For each of the following statements, write down the changes in energy stores that take place.** (4 marks, ★★★★)

a **A person base-jumping off the Eiffel Tower** ....

b **A gas fire** ....

c **Shooting a stone from a catapult** ....

d **Boiling water in an electric kettle** ....

WORKIT!

Describe the changes in the way energy is stored if a rocket is fired. Explain the journey until it runs out of fuel. (3 marks, ★★★)

Before the rocket is launched the chemical store is full. (1) ◄———

> Remember to break questions into short sentences. This will make your question easier to mark for the examiner.

At the instant the fuel is lit the chemical store begins to empty and kinetic and thermal stores fill. (1)

As the rocket goes higher its gravitational store increases. The kinetic store will also keep increasing until the rocket runs out of fuel. If the fuel is burned at the same rate, the thermal store will remain fairly constant, but some of the thermal energy store will be dissipated to the surroundings. (1)

DOIT!

Practise the mnemonic you have learned. Can you remember what every letter stands for? **T**homas **N**ever **E**ats **C**arrots **G**ranny **E**ats **M**any.

NAILIT!

Do not confuse energy resources with energy stores.

Energy resources are: nuclear, coal, gas, oil, geothermal, tidal, wind, wave, biofuels, and hydroelectric.

Think of your own mnemonic to learn the ways of generating energy.

Efficiency

1. a **State the efficiency equation.** (1 mark, ★★★)

....

b **State the two ways of stating a value of efficiency.** (2 marks, ★★★★)

....

....

2. **Complete the table below. The first example has been done for you.** (3 marks, ★★★)

Device or situation	Initial energy store	Final energy store
Catapult	Elastic	Kinetic
A go-kart freewheeling down a hill		
A car going uphill		
A growing plant		

3. **An MP3 changes 500 joules of energy via electrical work to 360 joules of useful energy stores. How efficient is it?** (2 marks, ★★★★)

....

....

....

4. **What is the efficiency of a van that requires 5000 joules of energy from its chemical store to transfer 900 joules to its kinetic store?** (2 marks, ★★★★)

....

....

....

NAILIT!

An energy transfer will never be 100% efficient in practice. In a laboratory or practical situation some energy is always dissipated, increasing the thermal store of the air around us.

National and global energy resources

(1) **The table below lists some renewable and non-renewable sources of energy.**

Source	Renewable?	Requires burning
Geothermal Power	Yes	No
Coal		
Biofuels	Yes/No	Yes
Oil		
Uranium		
Wave Power		
Solar Farms		
Wind Power		
Hydroelectricity		

Complete the table above to show whether each source:

a **Is renewable.** (4 marks, ★★)

b **Needs to be burned.** (1 mark, ★★★)

(2) **Why are biofuels identified as both renewable and non-renewable?** (1 mark, ★★★★)

....

....

DOIT!

Make your own flashcards on each way of generating energy. Remember to include advantages, disadvantages and show a basic understanding of how each method works.

NAILIT!

Make sure you can explain the advantages and disadvantages of different ways of generating energy. Remember to go into detail. Don't say 'wind energy is free'. Say 'once the initial investment and maintenance is covered, it is free'. Don't say 'tidal energy doesn't cause pollution'. Say 'tidal energy does not emit greenhouse gases, so it doesn't contribute to climate change'.

(3) The graph below shows how the power output from a wind turbine changes with wind speed.

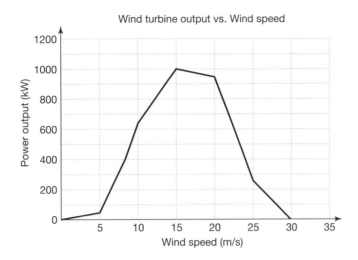

a At what wind speed is the power at a maximum? (2 marks, ★★★)

....

....

b If this maximum power output was constant, how many of these wind turbines would be needed to provide a total power output of 10 MW? (2 marks, ★★★)

....

....

c Why is it unlikely that a wind farm would produce a constant power output? (1 mark, ★★★)

....

....

(4) State one advantage and one disadvantage that wind power has compared to power from burning fossil fuel. (2 marks, ★★★)

....

....

....

Standard circuit diagram symbols

(1) Name and draw a component in the box that matches the description. (4 marks, ★★★★)

1 Used to measure current	**(A)** Ammeter
2 Changes resistance with light intensity	
3 Only lets current flow in one direction	
4 Can be used to vary resistance	
5 A safety component that melts when the current gets too high	

(2) A student wants to get the _I–V_ characteristic for a filament lamp.

a Draw a circuit diagram to show the components they would use. (2 marks, ★★★★★)

b Explain the method they would use to carry out the experiment. (6 marks, ★★★★★)

....

....

....

....

....

....

NAILIT!

Remember that a cell and a battery are both power supplies, but a battery is two or more cells joined together.

DOIT!

The only way to learn the circuit symbols is to keep drawing and redrawing them. Use a ruler and a 5p or 1p coin to draw ammeters, voltmeters, light dependent resistors and diodes.

Electrical charge and current

(1) State the equation linking charge, current and time. (1 mark, ★★)

....

(2) Complete the following sentences. (6 marks, ★★★)

.... is the name given to the flow of negatively .... particles around a

closed circuit. These particles are called .... Because of their charge they are

attracted to the .... terminal of a cell or .... In books we refer to the

opposite direction and call this .... current flow. This is where the current flows from

the positive to negative terminal of the power supply.

conventional	charged	electrons	positive	current
energy	alternating	protons	negative	battery

(3) Use the formula that links charge, current and time to complete the table. (4 marks, ★★★)

Charge (C)	Current (A)	Time (s)
10	10	1
40	2	
10	2	
100		500
	6	150

DO IT!

Make a mnemonic to learn difficult symbols such as Q for charge. An example is: the **Q**ueen is in **C**harge. Remember if you make your own, you will remember them much more easily.

WORKIT!

A reading light is switched on for 1 hour. It works on a current of 0.25 A. How much charge flowed in 1 hour? (2 marks, ★★)

Charge flow = current × time = or Q = It ◄── Choose the right equation.

1 hour = 60 × 60 = 3600 s ◄── You have to convert hours to seconds.

Q = It

= 0.25 A × 3600 (1)

= 900 C (1)

Substitute the values in the equation.

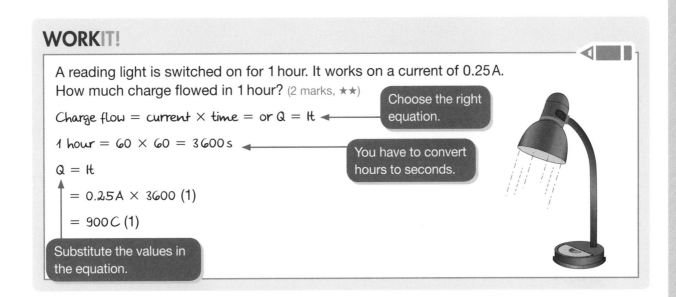

④ **In an electrolysis experiment a current of 6 A was passed through some copper sulfate solution. During this time a charge of 1800 C flowed through the copper sulfate solution.**

Calculate how long the current flowed through the copper sulfate in seconds and in minutes. (3 mark, ★★★)

....

....

....

....

NAILIT!

Topic link: you will have learned about electrolysis in chemistry.

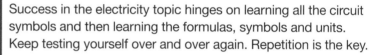

NAILIT!

Success in the electricity topic hinges on learning all the circuit symbols and then learning the formulas, symbols and units. Keep testing yourself over and over again. Repetition is the key.

For example:
What does Q stand for?
What is the unit for Q?
What does I stand for?
What is the unit for I?
What does V stand for? etc.

Current, resistance and potential difference and resistors

1 **a** **State the equation linking potential difference, current and resistance.** (1 mark, ★★)

....

b **What is this equation called?** (1 mark, ★★)

....

c **What condition needs to be present for it to work?** (1 mark, ★)

....

2 **The diagram below shows part of an electric circuit.** (4 marks, ★★★★)

Complete the circuit diagram by adding:

a **A variable resistor in series with the battery.**

b **A fixed resistor in series with the battery.**

c **A voltmeter that measures the potential difference across the fixed resistor.**

d **An ammeter in series that measures the total current in the series circuit.**

3 **Explain how the experimental set-up in the question above could be used to find the resistance of the fixed resistor.** (6 marks, ★★★★)

Include the following: how equipment is used, which measurements are taken, and how results are analysed to plot a graph.

....

....

....

....

....

....

④ **The resistance vs temperature graph for one type of electrical component is drawn below.**

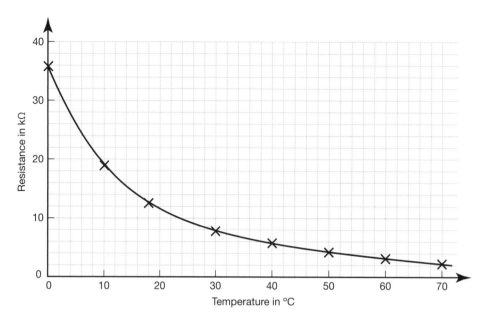

a **What component would have this relationship?** (1 mark, ★★)

....

b **Complete the diagram to show a circuit that can be used to make a results table of resistance vs temperature for the device.** (4 marks, ★★★★)

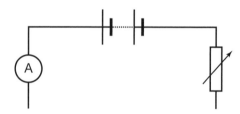

NAILIT!

Use the correct circuit symbol for each component that you add to the diagram.

NAILIT!

Knowing the *I–V* characteristics for the following components is essential: wire, resistor, filament lamp and diode.

Make sure that you know how to get the data from an experiment and then how you would plot a graph of *I–V* to observe whether the component always follows Ohm's law.

Which of those 4 components are ohmic and which are non-ohmic?

c i **What other measuring device would you need to gather the data for the graph, and how would you control the temperature?** (2 marks, ★★★)

....

....

ii **Use the graph to find out the resistance of the device at 10°C.** (2 marks, ★★★)

....

....

iii **How could the device be used in a practical application?** (1 mark, ★★★)

....

(5) **Calculate the total resistance in the following resistor combination.** (2 marks, ★★★)

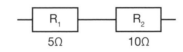

....

....

(6) **In the following circuit V_1 = 5V and A_1 = 1A. Complete the missing values.** (2 marks, ★★★)

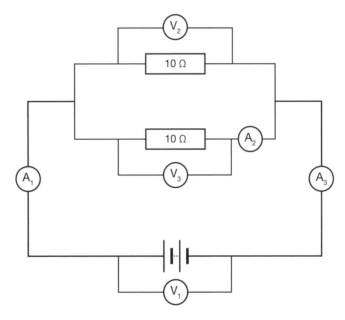

A_2 = ... A_3 = ... V_2 = ... V_3 = ...

DO IT!

Practise sketching the *I–V* graph for a component that follows Ohm's law. Annotate how you would work out the resistance of the component if the graph is a straight line.

Remember that if you put potential difference on the x-axis and current on the y-axis, then the gradient will not be the resistance.

It will be the reciprocal of the resistance or $\dfrac{1}{\text{resistance}}$.

Series and parallel circuits

(1) **Complete the sentences with the words below. Each word can be used only once.**
(5 marks, ★★★)

In a series circuit, current is the .... throughout the circuit and potential difference .... across the components. In a parallel circuit, ... is the same across each branch of the circuit and current splits through the parallel branches. An ammeter must be connected in .... to work correctly. A voltmeter must be connected in .... to work correctly.

series	splits	potential difference	resistance	current
parallel	same	energy	circuit	battery

(2) **Draw series circuits in the three boxes below with the following instructions. A complete circuit that contains:**

a **One bulb, one cell and a switch.** (2 marks, ★★)

b **Two cells (connected together correctly) and three bulbs. Connect an ammeter to measure the circuit current.** (3 marks, ★★★)

c **A battery, thermistor and bulb. Connect a voltmeter to measure the potential difference of the thermistor.** (4 marks, ★★★★)

a

b

c

(3) **Draw parallel circuits in the boxes below with the following instructions. A complete circuit that contains:**

a **One battery, two bulbs in parallel and a switch that switches off both bulbs.** (2 marks, ★★)

b **One battery, three bulbs in parallel and a switch that only switches off one bulb.** (2 marks, ★★★★)

c **A battery, bulb and thermistor in series and a bulb connected in parallel with the thermistor.** (2 marks, ★★★★)

a

b

c

NAILIT!

Knowing how to draw parallel and series circuits is really important. Make sure you practise drawing them. Remember:

A **series** circuit means one loop only. **Ammeters** are always connected in **series**.

A **parallel** circuit means more than one loop. **Voltmeters** are always connected in **parallel**.

(4) **Explain why all the lights in a house can be switched off separately in different rooms.** (2 marks, ★★★)

....

....

....

NAILIT!

Learn these rules: **current is the same in a series circuit** and **potential difference splits in a series circuit**.

Then for a parallel circuit it is just the opposite: **potential difference is the same** (across each branch) **in a parallel circuit** and **current splits in a parallel circuit**.

Mains electricity: direct and alternating potential difference (dc/ac)

(1) **a** **What do the terms dc and ac stand for?** (2 marks, ★★★)

....

b **Describe the difference between ac and dc.** (2 marks, ★★★)

....

....

(2) **Explain why we have to use ac for domestic supply.** (4 marks, ★★★★)

....

....

....

(3) **What type of potential difference is being supplied in the diagram to the right? What is the potential difference's value if each square represents 2 V?** (2 marks, ★★★★)

....

....

....

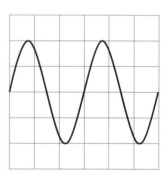

(4) **An ac source is connected to an oscilloscope. The waveform of the alternating potential difference from the source is displayed on the oscilloscope screen to the right.**

The Y-gain setting of the oscilloscope is 5 V/square. Determine the amplitude of the alternating potential difference. (2 marks, ★★★★★)

....

....

....

DO IT!

Learn the definitions for ac and dc, and explain the difference using a diagram. In one of them the current travels in one direction. In the other the current changes direction 50 times every second. Which is which?

NAIL IT!

Small portable devices generally run on dc, for example, laptops, torches, and mobile phones.

Larger domestic appliances or heaters usually run on ac, for example fridges, ovens, freezers, and toasters.

Mains electricity

(1) **Complete the gaps using the words below.** (3 marks, ★★)

The .... supplied to our homes is called .... electricity and it is an ....
current supply. This type of current .... direction many times per second. In fact the
current goes forwards and back .... times per second. This means it has a ....
of 50 Hz.

frequency	changes	fifty	alternating	mains	one hundred
electricity	direct	wavelength	charge	domestic	

(2) **Complete the labels on the following diagram of the plug.** (4 marks, ★★★)

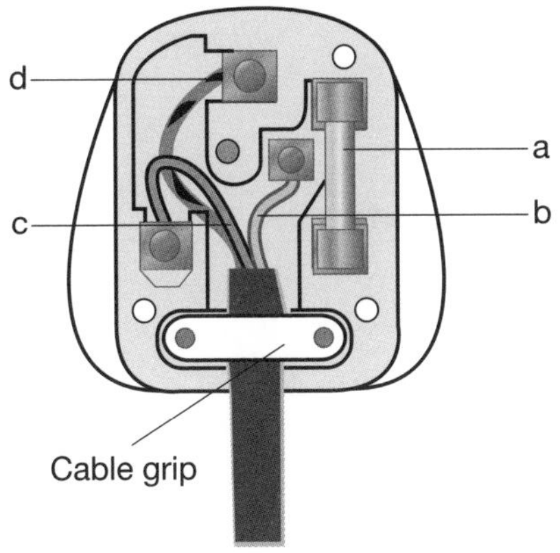

a ....

b ....

c ....

d ....

Cable grip

DO IT!

Practise drawing the inside of a plug and make an effort to remember the colour and main job of each cable.

(3) **Explain the role of the following in mains electricity and give the typical potential difference values for them when the circuit is working correctly.**

a Earth wire (1 mark, ★★★) ....

....

b Live wire (1 mark, ★★★) ....

....

c Neutral wire (1 mark, ★★★) ....

....

(4) **a Explain why a live wire may be dangerous even if a switch in the live circuit is open.** (2 marks, ★★★)

....

....

b Explain why it is not necessary to connect an earth wire to a device that has a plastic casing. (2 marks, ★★★)

NAILIT!

Sockets and the cases of plugs are generally made out of hard plastic. Plastic is used because it is a very good electrical insulator and can be moulded to completely surround the cables.

....

Electric power (with electrical devices)

(1) **State three formulas for calculating power.** (3 marks, ★★★)

....

....

....

(2) **A 20 V battery supplies 2 A through a resistor. Calculate the power dissipated in the resistor.** (3 marks, ★★)

....

....

....

NAILIT!

Take the time to learn all those equations. Unless you are confident with the equations you can only access about 60% of the marks in the electricity section of the paper.

(3) **A torch has a current of 0.1 A and has a resistance of 100 Ω. What is its power rating?** (2 marks, ★★★)

....

....

(4) **A 10 kW electric fire consumes 36 MJ of energy.**

How long is it on for in seconds and hours? (3 marks, ★★★★)

....

....

....

WORKIT!

A 25 kW shower is turned on for 3 minutes. Calculate the energy transferred in MJ to the water, assuming there is no dissipation of energy to the pipes or to the air in the room. (3 marks, ★★)

Energy transferred = power × time = P × t ◄— Choose the correct equation.

25 kW = 25 000 W ◄—

Remember to check for units and prefixes that require attention.

3 minutes = 180 s (1)

P × t = 25 000 W × 180 s ◄— Substitute in the values.

= 4 500 000 J (1)

To convert to MJ divide by 1 000 000 → $\dfrac{4\,500\,000}{(1\,000\,000)}$ = 4.5 MJ (1)

Energy transfers in appliances

1. **State two formulas for calculating energy.** (2 marks, ★★)

....

....

2. **Complete the following sentences. Each word can only be used once.** (3 marks, ★★★)

Everyday electrical .... are designed to bring about .... transfers. The .... of energy an appliance .... depends on how .... the appliance is switched on for and the .... of the appliance.

amount	transfers	long	energy	charge
appliances	power	heat	symbols	size

3. a **A 20 V internet digital radio is switched on and a charge of 500 C flows. How much energy is transferred?** (2 marks, ★★★)

....

....

b **The radio above had a constant current of 2 A. How long was the radio switched on for?** (2 marks, ★★★)

....

....

4. **An electric toothbrush operates at 12 V and draws a current of 2 A. It is used for 2 minutes. Calculate:**

a **The toothbrush's resistance.** (3 marks, ★★)

....

....

b **The charge flowing through the toothbrush in 2 minutes.** (3 marks, ★★★)

....

....

c **The energy supplied to the toothbrush in 2 minutes.** (3 marks, ★★★)

....

....

....

NAILIT!

Remember the unit for energy is the joule, and the unit for power is the watt.

1 watt is also equivalent to 1 joule/second. This is because:

$$\text{Power} = \frac{\text{energy}}{\text{time}} = \frac{E}{t}$$

So sometimes you might see J/s instead of W. These two units are interchangeable.

The National Grid

(1) **Label a to f in the diagram below with the following words.** (3 marks ★★)

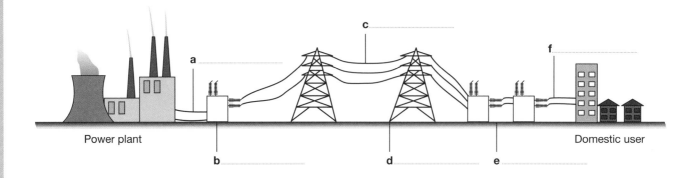

Power plant

Domestic user

230 V	60 Hz	675 kV	2.3 kV	pylon
step-up transformer	step-down transformer	step-up transducer	underground cables	step-down transducer

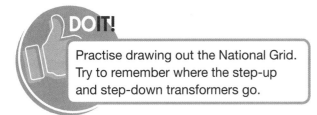

DO IT!

Practise drawing out the National Grid. Try to remember where the step-up and step-down transformers go.

NAIL IT!

You don't need to remember the exact values of potential difference except for domestic supply which is 230 V at 50 Hz.

(2) **Explain how increasing the potential difference in power transmission reduces power losses. You could refer to the equations $P = I^2 R$ or $P = VI$.** (3 marks, ★★★★)

....

....

....

....

(3) **A student tries to make a model of the National Grid, it looks like the circuit below.**

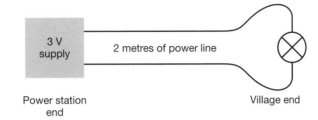

a **Explain why the bulb is very dim when the circuit is set up like this.** (1 mark, ★★★)

....

....

b **He improves the design and sets up a circuit like the one below. Why is the bulb now bright? Explain the roles of transformers A and B in the circuit.** (4 marks, ★★★★)

....

....

....

....

....

NAILIT!

Remember that to transfer electrical energy over long distances we need to step-up the potential difference to a higher value. The **power** is constant and we can use the power formula $P = IV$ to explain that if **voltage** goes up, current goes down. If we then put a really small current into another formula for power, $P = I^2 R$. The power losses through heating of the cable are much smaller. Think about it. Try squaring a really small number (a number less than 1) using your calculator and see what happens.

Static charge and electric fields (1)

(1) The picture shows an investigation of static electricity. A girl rubs a balloon on her head so the balloon gains a negative charge. She then holds the balloon close to her head, and her hair rises.

a **Explain, in terms of moving charges, how the balloon becomes negatively charged.** (2 marks, ★★★)

....

....

b **Explain why the girl's hair rises.** (2 marks, ★★★)

....

....

c **Later the balloon is placed against a wall and it stays 'stuck' to the wall. Explain why.** (2 marks, ★★★)

....

....

d **Explain why the balloon won't stay there for as long if the air is damp.** (1 mark, ★★★★)

....

NAILIT!

Success in statics questions is mostly about using the following key words with confidence: electrons, friction, insulator, conductor, earth, positive, negative, like, unlike, repel, attract, discharge, and so on.

Remember that in the question it is always something to do with the movement of electrons from one place to another!

Write the answer in short sentences and focus on using key words.

WORKIT!

Explain why the powder paint that leaves a spray paint machine spreads out.

How can static electricity be used to make the paint stick to a car body? (3 marks, ★★)

Friction between the paint and plastic paint nozzle transfers electrons from paint to paint nozzle. The paint powder is now positively charged. (1)

The positively charged paint repels itself as like charges repel. The paint spreads out evenly. (1)

The car is connected to an earth cable so compared to the paint is negatively charged. The positive paint is attracted to the negatively charged car. (1)

Static charge and electric fields (2)

(1) **Complete the following sentences. Each word can only be used once.** (3 marks, ★★★)

A .... object creates an .... field around itself. For example, a car can become

charged because of .... removing electrons from it and .... them to dust

particles as the car is moving through .... This would leave the car with a ....

electric field.

charged	friction	electric	uncharged	transferring
positive	air	force	conduction	negative

(2) **a Draw a diagram of the electric field pattern around the proton below.** (2 marks, ★★)

$$\text{(P)}$$

b Another proton is brought towards the first proton. Sketch the field lines. (3 marks, ★★★★)

$$\text{(P)} \quad \text{(P)}$$

(3) **Use ideas about fields to explain how a lightning rod works.** (3 marks, ★★★★)

....

....

....

DOIT!

Practise drawing field lines for these situations:

- positively or negatively charged objects on their own
- two positively charged objects
- two negatively charged objects
- two objects with opposite charges.

NAILIT!

- Electric field lines always go from positive to negative.
- Field lines never cross.
- The further apart the field lines, the weaker the field.
- The closer together the field lines, the stronger the field.

Particle model of matter and density of materials

(1) **Complete the sentences. Some of the words can be used more than once.** (6 marks, ★★★)

The formula for density is .... divided by .... and the standard SI unit is

.... Sometimes the values are very large so .... are used instead. A density of

.... kg/m³ is equal to the density of .... g/cm³. This is also the density of water.

1000	kg/m³	force	1	g/cm³
area	newtons	mass	1 000 000	volume

(2) **A metal block has a volume of 0.005 m³ and mass of 56.5 kg.**

a **Calculate the density of the metal block in kg/m³.** (2 marks, ★★★)

....

b **Convert the density to g/cm³.** (1 mark, ★★★★)

....

(3) **A large wooden block has a volume 8000 cm³ and density of 600 kg/m³.**

Calculate the mass of the wooden block in kg. (3 marks, ★★★★)

....

....

(4) **A small stone of mass of 18 g is lowered into a measuring cylinder.**

The water level increases from 20.0 to 27.5 ml.

Calculate the density of the stone in g/cm³. (4 marks, ★★★★)

....

....

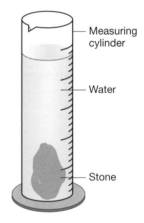

— Measuring cylinder

— Water

— Stone

DO IT!

Make an effort to learn the symbol and units for density. The symbol is ρ and is pronounced 'rho' and it is from the Greek alphabet. The units for density are generally g/cm³ or kg/m³. Make sure you can convert between the two.

NAILIT!

Don't get confused with conversions between m³ → mm³ and m³ → cm³ and vice versa.

Remember 1 m = 100 cm   or   1 m = 1000 mm

$1 m^3 = 1 m \times 1 m \times 1 m = 1 m^3$

$1 m^3 = 100 cm \times 100 cm \times 100 cm = 1 000 000 cm^3$ (or $10^6 cm^3$)

$1 m^3 = 1000 mm \times 1000 mm \times 1000 mm = 1 000 000 000 mm^3$ (or $10^9 mm^3$)

Changes of state and internal energy

(1) **Marbles in a box are a good model to represent the molecules in a solid, liquid and a gas. Explain which box best represents each state of matter and briefly explain why.**
(6 marks, ★★★★)

A   B   C

A ....

B ....

C ....

(2) **Explain why the temperature of a window increases when water condenses onto its surface.** (3 marks, ★★★★)

....

....

(3) **What term describes the type of change when ice melts and becomes water? Tick one box.** (1 mark, ★★)

Physical	
Chemical	
Sublimation	
Radiation	

WORKIT!

If alcohol is dropped onto the back of your hand, why does it make your hand feel cool? (4 marks, ★★★★)

Your hand is warm (higher thermal store) and the alcohol has a lower temperature (lower thermal store). A difference in temperature between two touching objects causes the hotter object's thermal store to go down and the colder object's thermal store to go up. (1)

The thermal store of the hand goes down (reducing the temperature) and the thermal store of the alcohol goes up (increasing the temperature). (1)

The increase in the thermal store of the alcohol causes the alcohol to evaporate (alcohol has a fairly low boiling point, so it evaporates at a lower temperatures than water, for example). (1)

Evaporation of alcohol causes a reduction of the energy store in your hand, decreasing the internal energy of your hand. This makes your hand feel cool. (1)

NAILIT!

Practise drawing the diagrams for liquids, solids and gases. Remember to do the following:

- Draw particles as circles and make them all approximately the same size.
- The particles in solids are ordered in straight rows and are touching on all sides. The gaps between them are very small.
- The particles in liquids are still touching, but are not as organised and look a little chaotic. They still fill the container and no gaps are bigger than the particles themselves.
- For gases draw very few atoms that are far apart.

Changes of temperature and specific latent heat

(1) **State the formula for specific latent heat.** (1 mark, ★★)

....

....

(2) **The following diagram represents energy supplied in kJ by a heater to increase the temperature of water from below 0°C to above 100°C.**

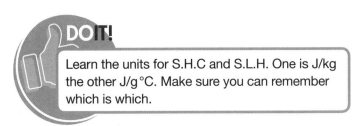

What happens to the energy of the particles of the solid/liquid in each state-change as more energy is supplied by heating? (6 marks, ★★★★)

....

....

....

....

....

....

(3) **Calculate the energy in kJ required to melt 100g of ice. The specific latent heat of fusion for ice is 334 000 J/kg.** (3 marks, ★★★★)

....

....

....

> **NAILIT!**
>
> Don't confuse specific heat capacity (S.H.C) with specific latent heat (S.L.H). Specific heat capacity is the energy required to increase the temperature of a kilogram of a substance by 1°C. Specific latent heat is the energy required to melt, or turn to gas 1 kg of a substance without changing the temperature.

> **DOIT!**
>
> Learn the units for S.H.C and S.L.H. One is J/kg the other J/g °C. Make sure you can remember which is which.

Particle motion in gases (1)

(1) **Complete the gaps with the words below.** (6 marks, ★★★)

The molecules of gas are in constant .... motion. The average .... energy

of the .... is proportional to temperature on the .... scale. Changing the

temperature of a gas in a container of fixed volume will change the .... exerted on the

sides of the ....

kinetic	random	Celsius	container	kelvin
ordered	gravitational potential		particles	pressure

(2) **This diagram shows a sealed box filled with oxygen molecules.**

Describe the motion of the molecules. (2 marks, ★★)

....

....

....

(3) **Define internal energy.** (2 marks, ★★★)

....

....

....

WORKIT!

This diagram shows the kinetic energy of the different gas molecules in a sealed container.

Some of the gas condenses on a cool side of the container.

Referring to the graph explain why the temperature of the remaining gas would initially increase. (4 marks, ★★)

The slower moving molecules would condense onto the surface more readily, as they would require less energy to change from a gas into a liquid. (1)

Molecules with higher kinetic energy (E_k) would remain. (1)

The kinetic energy, or E_k of molecules, is proportional to temperature (in kelvins). (1)

As more higher speed molecules remain, the average temperature will go up. (1)

DOIT!

Remember that when doing these calculations, unless you are calculating a temperature change, it is always necessary to convert degrees Celsius (°C) into kelvin (K). ◄

A helpful rhyme to learn the conversion is 'K is C plus 273' for K = °C + 273.

Particle motion in gases (2)

(1) **State the equation that links pressure and volume in gases.** (1 mark, ★★★)

....

(2) **The initial temperature of a gas trapped in a container is –23°C. The container is heated and the final temperature of the gas is 477°C.**

   a **Calculate the temperature change in °C and then state it in kelvins.** (2 marks, ★★★)

....

....

   b **What is the change in kinetic energy of the particles in the gas?** (2 marks, ★★★★)

....

....

(3) **A gas has an initial volume of 120 cm³ at a pressure of 75 kPa.**

Assume that the temperature remains constant.

Calculate the final volume of this gas if pressure is increased to 225 kPa. (3 marks, ★★★★)

....

....

....

(4) **When a bicycle pump is used to pump up a tyre, the pump starts to feel warm. Explain why this happens.** (3 marks, ★★★★)

....

....

....

NAILIT!

Work done = energy transferred

If we do work on a gas it increases the internal energy of the gas molecules, and this leads to an increase in temperature (remember, E_k is proportional to temperature).

DOIT!

Make sure you learn the units for pressure. The standard unit is the pascal, abbreviated to Pa, which is equivalent to N/m².

The structure of the atom (1)

(1) Complete the following sentences. (3 marks, ★★)

a The atom is composed of 3 subatomic particles: ...., ... and

....

b The centre of the atom is called the .... and contains .... and

....

c An atom contains the same number of .... and .... and has a

.... charge.

(2) The diagram shows a simplified helium atom. Insert on the diagram the missing names of the subatomic particles. (3 marks, ★★)

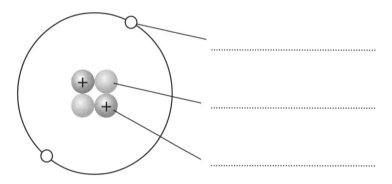

....

....

....

(3) Complete the table below. (4 marks, ★★)

Particle	Symbol	Relative mass	Charge
Proton	p		+1
Neutron	n	1	
Electron	e⁻		

NAILIT!

Ideas about the atom have evolved over the centuries. Make sure that you understand the basics of each model.

(4) Describe our current understanding of the nuclear model of the atom. Make particular reference to the following: radius, size of atom, electron arrangement and mass of atom. (6 marks, ★★★★)

....

....

....

....

....

The structure of the atom (2)

(1) **State how many protons, neutrons and electrons there are in the atoms below.** (6 marks, ★★★)

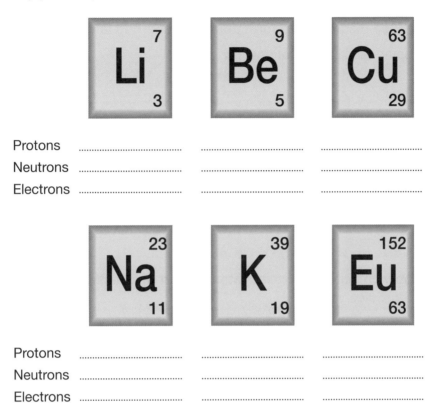

Protons ....
Neutrons ....
Electrons ....

Protons ....
Neutrons ....
Electrons ....

(2) **Complete the sentences below. Some words may be used twice.** (6 marks, ★★★)

An .... is an atom with the same number of .... and a different number

of ....

.... have the same chemical properties as the atom. If the .... number

is altered, the .... changes.

isotope	electrons	protons	different	neutrons	isotopes
	electron	ion	ions	atomic	element

NAILIT!

Atoms are neutral. This means they have the same number of protons and electrons. If they lose or gain electrons we call this ionisation. Remember that atoms cannot lose or gain protons or neutrons as easily. A change in the number of protons and neutrons is a nuclear process.

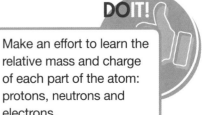

DOIT!

Make an effort to learn the relative mass and charge of each part of the atom: protons, neutrons and electrons.

③ **Circle true (T) or false (F) for the following statements.** (4 marks, ★★★★)

    a To form an ion you have to remove a proton from an atom.   T   F

    b An ion can be formed by gaining or removing an electron.   T   F

    c Metal atoms lose electron(s) to form positively charged ions.   T   F

    d Non-metal atoms lose electrons to form negatively charged ions.   T   F

WORKIT!

These chlorine atoms have different mass numbers.

a How can this be explained? (2 marks, ★)

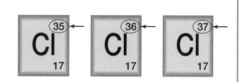

The mass number is different but the atomic number is the same. (1)

This can only mean one thing. They are isotopes of chlorine. (1)

b Why is the mass number of chlorine commonly stated as 35.5? (3 marks, ★★)

In nature there are three different naturally occurring isotopes of chlorine. (1)

The isotopes have different mass numbers, 35.5 is the weighted average. (1)

This does not mean that any of the isotopes have 35.5 protons and neutrons. (1)

Developing a model of the atom

1. In the early part of the 20th century, scientists thought that the atom was like a 'plum pudding'. They used this model to explain the internal structure of the atom.

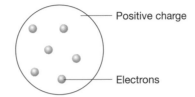

Plum pudding model

Describe the main features of the plum pudding model that were put forward to explain the internal structure of the atom. (3 marks, ★★★★)

....

....

....

2. An experiment, designed to investigate the 'plum pudding' model, involved firing alpha particles at thin gold foil leaf.

The diagram shows the main paths, A, B and C, of several thousand alpha particles. The results are expressed as percentages.

Explain what each of the paths A, B and C tells us about the atom. Your ideas should reference why the plum pudding model was wrong. (6 marks, ★★★★★)

Path A: Very small deflection of 0 to 4 degrees was taken by approximately 62% of the alpha particles.

Path B: Small to medium sized deflection of 4 to 30 degrees were taken by approximately 38%.

Path C: Large deflection of more than 120 degrees or backscattering was taken by only 0.01% of the alpha particles.

Gold nucleus

....

....

....

....

....

....

....

....

....

....

Radioactive decay and nuclear radiation

(1) Fill in the missing words in the paragraph below, using words from the box. (6 marks, ★★★)

Some atomic nuclei are .... The nucleus emits .... as it changes to

become more stable. This is a .... process called radioactive ....

Activity is the rate at which a source of .... nuclei decays. Activity is measured in

.... (Bq).

decay	becquerel(s)	stable	random	radioactive
waste	radiation	unstable	fusion	fission

(2) Complete the table below about alpha, beta and gamma radiation. (3 marks, ★★★)

Radiation type	What it is made of?	What stops it?	Ionising effect
Alpha			Highly ionising
Beta		A few millimetres of aluminium	
Gamma	High energy EM wave		

(3) The following diagram shows how beta radiation can be used to make sure paper is made with a fairly constant thickness.

a Why is beta suitable for this task, and not alpha or gamma? (2 marks, ★★★)

....

....

....

Rollers

Source of beta radiation

Paper pulp

Sheet of paper

Detector

Signal sent to computer which controls the rollers

Feedback to rollers

b How does feedback ensure that paper is of uniform thickness? (2 marks, ★★★)

....

....

NAILIT!

The unit for activity is the becquerel. The becquerel is equivalent to 1 disintegration, or decay of one nucleus, per second. Activity cannot be detected directly but can be estimated with a Geiger–Muller tube, which measures count-rate. Count-rate can also be stated as 'number of counts per minute, hour, day or year'. Whereas activity is always in Bq – nuclear disintegrations **per second**. Count-rate and activity are not always the same because the Geiger–Muller tube has a dead time in which it doesn't detect some nuclear disintegrations.

DOIT!

Alpha (α), beta (β) and gamma (γ) are the three kinds of radiation. For each one make sure you learn:

- What is it composed of?
- What stops it?
- How heavily ionising is it?
- Is it affected by magnetic fields?

Remember that there are two types of beta radiation: negative and positive.

Nuclear equations

(1) **Uranium-238 eventually decays to the stable isotope lead-208.**

All the steps in this process can be shown on a diagram. This is called a decay chain and the process takes several billion years. An example is shown below:

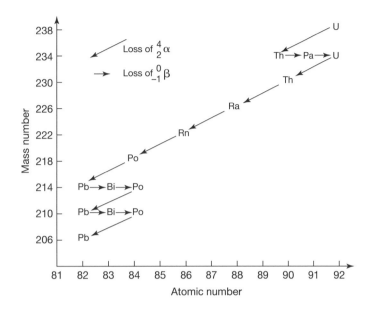

Use the mass number and atomic number references in the above decay chain to complete the following nuclear decay equations. Complete the mass and atomic number for each particle.

a $^{214}_{82}Pb \rightarrow \boxed{}Bi + \boxed{}_{-1}e$ (2 marks, ★★★)

b $^{214}_{84}Po \rightarrow \boxed{}Pb + \boxed{}He$ (2 marks, ★★★★)

c $^{230}_{90}Th \rightarrow$ (4 marks, ★★★★★)

NAILIT!

Changes take place in the atomic and mass numbers during alpha (α) and beta (β) decay, but not during gamma (γ) decay. In nuclear equations, make sure that the atomic numbers and mass numbers balance on each side of the equation.

DOIT!

You do not need to remember specific nuclear equations but you do need to be able to balance the mass and atomic numbers for nuclear equations for alpha (α) and beta (β) decays.

Complete the following example and state if it is an example of beta (β) or alpha (α) decay.

$$^{238}_{92}U \rightarrow \boxed{}Th + \boxed{}\boxed{}$$

To check your atomic and mass numbers refer back to graph of mass number vs atomic number.

Half-life of radioactive elements

(1) **Write a definition for the term half-life.** (2 marks, ★★★)

....

....

....

DO IT!

Learn the definition for half-life from memory. It often comes up in exams

(2) **A body was found in a bog in rural Ireland.**

A sample of bone from the body was analysed using radio-carbon dating techniques.

Once a living thing dies, the carbon-14 in its body decays. Carbon-14 has a half-life of 5700 years.

Consequently, archaeologists can use any material containing carbon to determine the age, such as bone, wood or leather.

a **If a bone contained $\frac{1}{4}$ of the expected carbon-14, how old would it be?** (3 marks, ★★★★)

....

....

....

b **If a bone contained $\frac{1}{16}$ of the expected carbon-14, how old would it be?** (3 marks, ★★★★)

....

....

c **Draw a sketch of the graph of the half-life. Assume an initial count-rate of 4000 cpm.**
(4 marks, ★★★★)

NAILIT!

If you are a Higher Tier student remember that you need to be able to express the net decline of radioactive isotopes as a **ratio**.

Hazards and uses of radioactive emissions (1)

1 There are **two** main ways in which people can be exposed to radiation.

State the **two** ways they can happen and the effects of radiation on body tissue.
(6 marks, ★★★★)

....

....

....

....

2 **a** What protective measures can be taken to protect those who regularly come into contact with radioactive sources? (5 marks, ★★★★)

....

....

....

....

....

b Why is it important for findings on the effects of radiation on humans to be published?
(2 marks, ★★★★)

....

....

3 This pie chart shows the main sources of background radiation in the UK. Each source contributes to the average yearly radiation dose.

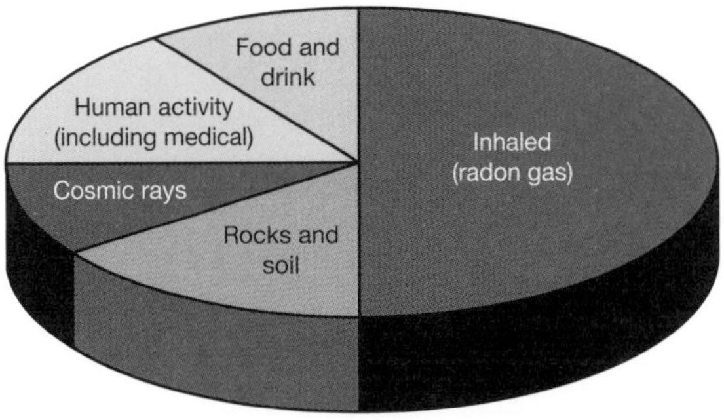

a What is meant by background radiation?
(1 mark, ★★)

....

....

Sources of background radiation

Food and drink
Human activity (including medical)
Cosmic rays
Inhaled (radon gas)
Rocks and soil

b Suggest why an astronaut is likely to get a higher dose of background radiation than the average person. (2 marks, ★★★)

....

....

....

DO IT!

Some background radiation is artificial but most is natural. Make sure you know three examples of each.

Hazards and uses of radioactive emissions (2)

(1) **The table below shows the different half-lives and type of decay for several radioactive isotopes.**

Radioactive isotope	Decay type	Half-life
Radium-226	Alpha	1600 years
Bismuth-214	Beta	20 minutes
Lead-210	Beta	22 years
Polonium-210	Alpha	138 days
Bismuth-210	Alpha, beta and gamma	5 days
Radon-222	Alpha	3.8 days

The initial count-rate of a sample of rock containing bismuth-214 is 4000 counts/minute. How many counts/minute would be detected 1 hour later? (2 marks, ★★★)

....

....

(2) **Radium-226 decays into radon-222 via alpha decay. A rock is found that once had a large deposit entirely made of radium-226. Now an eighth of the deposit is the original radium-226 but seven eighths of this part of the rock is filled with radon-222 gas.**

a How many half-lives have passed? (2 marks, ★★★★)

....

....

b How long has passed since all of the original radium-226 was present? (2 marks, ★★★)

....

....

DO IT!

Radioactive isotopes have many applications in our day-to-day lives: smoke alarms, treating cancer, destroying bacteria, detecting metal or paper thickness, as tracers and dating. Study these examples and make flashcards to help you remember.

NAILIT!

Radioactive isotopes can be alpha (α), beta (β) or gamma (γ) emitters. They emit this radiation to make their nuclei more stable. Half-lives can range from a fraction of a second to billions of years.

③ **Lead-210 decays via beta decay to bismuth-210. It has a half-life of 22 years.**

A sample is found that originally consisted completely of lead-210.

Now it exists with one lead-210 atom for every seven bismuth-210 atoms.

a **How many half-lives have passed?** (2 marks, ★★★★★)

....

....

b **How old is the sample?** (1 mark, ★★★)

....

WORKIT!

A safe level of radon-222 gas is 20 Bq. A house's basement contains trapped radon-222 gas which has an activity of 320 Bq. Building changes are made and radiation levels are checked by physicists. If no radon enters or leaves the basement, how long would it take the trapped radon-222 to reach safe levels? (3 marks, ★★)

The original activity is 320 Bq and the safe activity is 20 Bq. (1)

$320 \rightarrow 160 \rightarrow 80 \rightarrow 40 \rightarrow 20$ ◄——— How many times do you have to halve 320 to reach 20?

It had to be halved 4 times. (1)

This means 4 half-lives have elapsed.

4 half-lives = 4 × 3.8 days

    = 15.2 days (1)

Hazards and uses of radioactive emissions (3)

Radioactive isotope	Decay type	Half-life
Technetium-99	Gamma	6 hours
Xenon-133	Gamma	5 days
Strontium-90	Beta	28 years
Americium-241	Alpha	433 years
Protactinium-234	Beta	80 seconds

Answer questions 1 and 2 using the table above, and make reference to half-life and decay type in your answers.

(1) **Which type of radioactive isotope is used to investigate whether a person's liver is functioning correctly? Why is this type chosen?** (3 marks, ★★★★)

....

....

....

(2) a **Cobalt-60 is the most commonly used isotope to treat brain tumours. If it wasn't available, which type of radioactive isotope from the table would be the most suitable to kill cancer cells? Explain why.** (3 marks, ★★★★)

....

....

....

b **Cobalt-60 has a half-life of over 5 years. Why is this an advantage over the radioactive isotope you chose in part a?** (1 mark, ★★★)

....

(3) **Explain why the use of radiation to destroy cancerous cells is classed as a 'high risk method' for the treatment of cancer. What are the risks of chemotherapy and radiotherapy?** (4 marks, ★★★)

....

....

....

....

....

Nuclear fission and fusion

(1) **The diagram to the right shows what can happen when the nucleus of a uranium-235 atom absorbs a neutron.**

What name is given to the process shown in the diagram? (1 mark, ★★)

....

(2) **How do the mass number and atomic number of an atom change when its nucleus absorbs a neutron?** (2 marks, ★★★)

....

....

Neutron

U-235

Te-137   Zr-97

2 neutrons + energy

(3) **Explain why control rods are used in a nuclear fission reactor.** (3 marks, ★★★)

....

....

(4) a **Explain what fusion is.** (2 marks, ★★★)

....

....

b **Compare the similarities and differences between fission and fusion.** (6 marks, ★★★★)

....

....

....

....

....

WORKIT!

Explain why fusion does not take place at low temperatures and pressures. (2 marks, ★★★)

Protons are positively charged and exert a force of electrostatic repulsion on each other. (1) At low temperatures they are not moving fast enough and at low pressures they are not pushed close enough together for fusion to happen. (1)

Explain some of the difficulties of generating energy from the fusion process. (4 marks, ★★★★)

Extremely high temperatures and pressures are required. (1) This is very expensive and dangerous and requires very specialised containers. (1)

Very strong magnetic fields are required to contain the fusion fuel (plasma). (1)

The containment is challenging and if the plasma touches the container walls it will cool very rapidly and damage the walls. (1)

Forces and their interactions

① **Tick which of the following quantities is a vector.** (1 mark, ★★★)

Speed
Distance

☐

Energy
Velocity

☐

② **Draw lines to match the words to their definitions.** (4 marks, ★★★★)

1 Speed	a Has magnitude but no direction.
2 Velocity	b Has both magnitude and direction.
3 A scalar quantity	c Change in distance per unit time.
4 A vector quantity	d Change in displacement per unit time.

③ **A boy is pulling a trolley along the ground. Moving the trolley requires him to exert a force on the trolley. The arrow represents the force. What two pieces of information does the vector tell you about the force?** (2 marks, ★★★)

....

....

④ **An electrostatic force is a non-contact force.**

a **Describe the difference between a contact force and a non-contact force.** (2 marks, ★★★)

....

....

b **State two other non-contact forces.** (2 marks, ★★)

....

....

DOIT!

Learn the definition for scalar and vector and a couple of examples of each. Being asked to define vectors and scalars and provide examples of each is a common exam question.

NAILIT!

You need to be able to break a vector down into its vertical and horizontal components. This can be done graphically or by using trigonometry.

Gravity

(1) **State the formula and unit for weight.** (2 marks, ★★★)

....

(2) **Two students, Karen and Jane, are talking about mass and weight.**

Mass and weight are not the same and have different units.

Karen

Mass and weight are the same and are both measured in kg.

Jane

Explain which one of the students is correct. Compare mass and weight in your answer.
(6 marks, ★★★★)

....

....

....

....

....

(3) **An astronaut has a mass of 75 kg. He visits the Moon.**

The Moon has gravitational field strength of 1.6 N/kg

Calculate the astronaut's weight on the Moon. (2 marks, ★★)

....

....

....

 **NAILIT!**

Gravitational field strength is proportional to the mass of the planet the astronaut is on and inversely proportional to his or her distance from the centre of the planet.

The greater the mass → the greater the field strength.

The further from the centre of the planet → the lower the field strength.

 DOIT!

Learn the difference between mass and weight. This is one of the most common misunderstandings in physics. Don't be the person who gets it wrong!

Resultant forces

(1) Match the left side to the right side to complete the sentences below. (4 marks, ★★)

1 A resultant force is

2 A force is

3 When forces are balanced

4 A force can affect

5 The unit of force is

a one force that is the sum of all forces acting.

b the resultant force is zero.

c an object's motion or its shape.

d a push or a pull.

e the newton (N).

(2) Calculate the resultant force acting on each of the three boxes. (3 marks, ★★★)

(Arrows are not to scale and are only to indicate direction of the force.)

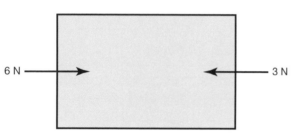

6 N → ← 3 N

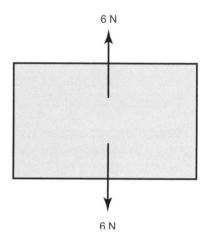

6 N

6 N

a ....

b ....

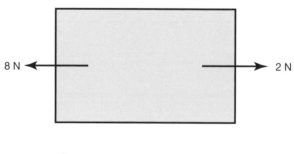

8 N ← → 2 N

c ....

 DOIT!

Practise drawing free body diagrams. Make sure you can do this for objects that are in water, on a solid surface or falling through air.

NAILIT!

Remember that if an object is moving with constant velocity, or if it is stationary, the vector forces must be all balanced. Make sure you are familiar with all the different forces. Here are a few examples: normal contact force, weight, drag, friction and upthrust.

③ **A duck is moving across a lake at a constant velocity.**

a **Add labelled arrows on the picture below to show the vector forces acting on the duck.** (3 marks, ★★★★)

upthrust	air resistance	friction	weight	thrust

b **The duck needed to accelerate to catch a tasty piece of bread.**

Describe and explain how these force vectors change. (4 marks, ★★★★★)

....

....

....

....

....

Work done and energy transfer

(1) **State the formula for work done.** (2 marks, ★★)

....

(2) **Which of the following units can be used for work done, as well as J or joules.** (1 mark, ★★★)

W
Nm

☐

N/m
J/s

☐

(3) **a A child pushes a go-kart with a force of 30 N. The go-kart moves 4 m along the floor. Calculate the work done on the go-kart.** (3 marks, ★★★)

....

....

....

....

b The child now does 240 J of work on the go-kart and pushes with the same force as in part a.

How far does the child have to push the go-kart to do 240 J of work? (3 marks, ★★★★)

....

....

....

....

c Would the temperature of the go-kart change? Explain your answer. (2 marks, ★★★)

....

....

....

....

DOIT!

Learn the formula and units for work done. Remember work done is equivalent to energy transfer. Does this help you remember the unit for work done?

NAILIT!

Remember that the symbol for the displacement is **s**, and it is often used for distance as well.

Forces and elasticity

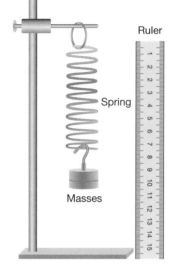

(1) **A student investigates by how much the extension of a spring changes when he suspends different slotted masses from it.**

The student finds that the spring's extension increases by the same length each time an additional slotted mass is added, as long as he only adds one mass at a time. Explain why. (2 marks, ★★)

....

....

....

(2) a **Label the axes below, and sketch a graph to show the behaviour of a spring under tension/when a force is applied to it.** (3 marks, ★★★)

b **How could you work out the spring constant from the graph of results?** (2 marks, ★★★★)

....

....

....

(3) **The student uses the same experimental procedure but this time hangs slotted masses from an elastic band.**

They conclude that the elastic band's extension is not always proportional to the force applied and undergoes inelastic deformation.

Explain what is meant by the term *inelastic* deformation. (2 marks, ★★★)

....

....

....

DO IT!

Make sure you are familiar with all the key words in this topic. What is the difference between elastic and inelastic deformation?

NAILIT!

To change the shape of an object by stretching, bending or compressing, there have to be at least two forces present.

Moments, levers and gears

(1) **Complete the following sentence with the words below.** (4 marks, ★★)

A force or a .... of forces can cause an object to .... The ....

effect of a force is also called the .... of the force.

momentum	rotate	system	turning	terminal	moment	float

(2) **Tick the correct unit for a moment.** (1 mark, ★★★★)

| Nm | ☐ |
| Ns | |

| kg/m³ | ☐ |
| kgm/s | |

(3) **A student predicts that the beam below would be balanced.**

Use a calculation to show whether they are correct. (3 marks, ★★★)

....

....

....

40N · 50N · 10m · 8m

NAILIT!

A moment is the force multiplied by the perpendicular distance from the pivot.

Remember to state the conservation of momentum law:
anticlockwise moments = clockwise moments.

DOIT!

All students find moments questions hard. The only solution is to keep practising the problems until you gain confidence.
Remember:

1 Choose a point on the beam.

2 Ignore the forces acting through that point.

3 Anticlockwise moments = clockwise moments.

WORKIT!

What distance must the 50N weight be from the pivot to balance the beam? (3 marks, ★★)

State equation

Force × distance = force × distance (1)

Substitute in the values

$4N \times 12m = 50N \times y$ (1)

Solve equation

$y = \frac{4 \times 12}{50} = 0.96m$ (1)

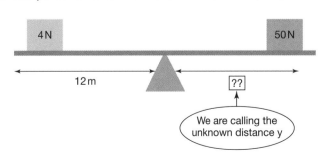

4N · 50N · 12m · ??

We are calling the unknown distance y

Pressure and pressure differences in a fluid (1)

(1) **State the equation used to calculate the pressure exerted by the surface of a liquid on an object.** (1 marks, ★★★)

....

(2) **Tick one box. A fluid can be either:** (1 mark, ★★★)

A solid or a liquid	
A solid or a gas	

A liquid or a gas	
A liquid or a cold metal	

(3) **Complete the following sentences.** (3 marks, ★★★)

The .... in fluids causes a force .... to any .... The pressure at

the surface of any fluid can be calculated using the equation

.... = .../.......................... .

parallel   density   mass   pressure   perpendicular   surface   mass   force   area   volume

(4) **The pressure at the surface of the Dead Sea is 106 kPa.**

A man floating on the Dead Sea has a surface area of 0.8 m² in the water.

Calculate the force exerted on his body by the water. (3 marks, ★★★★)

....

....

....

....

....

NAILIT!

The unit for pressure is either expressed as N/m² or Pa. Pa is the abbreviation for pascals. 1 Pa = 1 N/m².

NAILIT!

Make sure you can convert between the different units in area calculations.

1 000 000 mm² = 10 000 cm² = 1 m²

Pressure and pressure differences in a fluid (2)

1 **A boy dives to the bottom of a deep swimming pool.**

The pool has a depth of 3 m.

Calculate the pressure increase at the bottom of the swimming pool. (3 marks, ★★★)

Density of water = 1000 kg/m³

g = 10 N/kg

....

....

....

....

2 **A mountaineer takes a bag of crisps up a mountain as a special treat for reaching the summit. When she reaches the top she pulls her crisps out and finds that the bag has puffed up like a balloon.**

Why do you think this happened? Tick one box. (1 mark, ★★★★)

The air outside the packet has a higher temperature than the air inside the packet.	
The packet has a hole in it that allowed air from outside to enter.	
The increased ultraviolet on the bag gave the gas inside more energy.	
The air outside is now at a lower pressure than the air inside the packet.	

3 **Atmospheric pressure is approximately 100 kPa. Humans' ears contain air pockets.**

Explain why the boy's ears, in question 1, might hurt when he is at the bottom of the pool. (3 marks, ★★★★)

....

....

....

④ **A student has a large bottle full of water.**

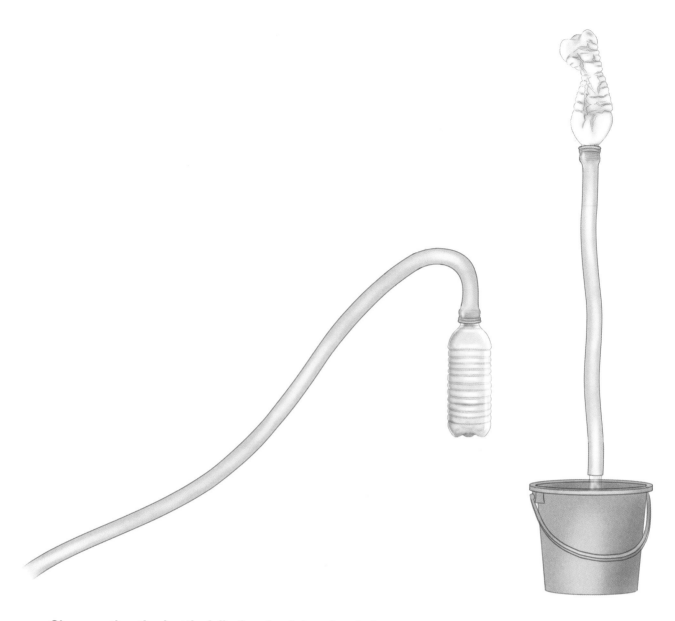

She empties the bottle full of water into a bucket.

As the water pours out of the long tube, the plastic bottle starts to crumple at the sides as shown in the diagram. Explain why this happens. (3 marks, ★★★★)

....

....

....

DOIT!

If you can do this safely, swim to the bottom of a swimming pool. Pay particular attention to the pressure you can feel in your ears and nose. Why does this happen?

NAILIT!

We live at the bottom of a large mass of air called the **atmosphere**. It exerts a huge pressure on us called 'atmospheric pressure'.

Distance, displacement, speed and velocity

1. A bird flies from point A on one fence to point B on another. It travels a route that is 18m long in total.

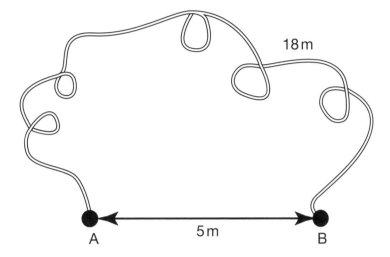

The diagram shows the route it took to get from A to B.

The 5m route is the shortest way to get from A to B.

a State the term used for the 18m route: .... (1 mark, ★★★)

b State the term used for the 5m route: .... (1 mark, ★★★)

2. Label the following distance time graphs with the following words. (3 marks, ★★★)

steady speed	acceleration	deceleration

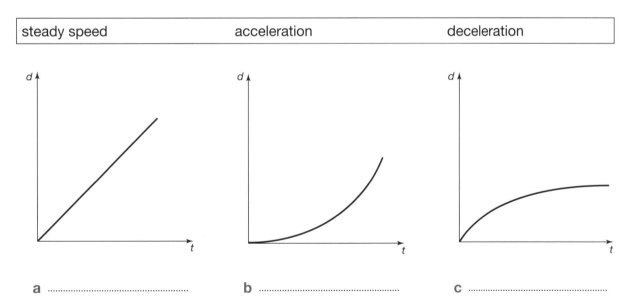

a ....

b ....

c ....

(3) **The following distance–time graph shows a car journey.**

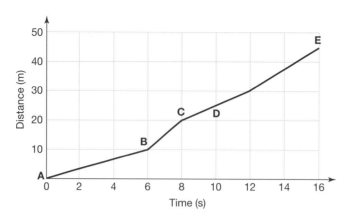

a **What is the total distance travelled on the journey?** (1 mark, ★★★)

....

b **Work out the speed from A to B on the graph.** (3 marks, ★★★)

....

....

c **Without making a calculation, how can you tell that the speed from B to C is higher than A to B?** (2 marks, ★★★★)

....

....

....

(4) **Match the following to their typical speeds. One has already been done for you.**
(4 marks, ★★★)

1 An aeroplane	**a** 5 m/s
2 Olympic sprinter	**b** 30 m/s
3 Cheetah	**c** 200 m/s
4 Mouse	**d** 10 m/s
5 Snail ———————	**e** 0.02 m/s

DO IT!

Practise drawing distance–time graphs and make sure you know how to represent the following: stationary or at rest, low steady speed, high steady speed, acceleration and deceleration.

NAILIT!

Learn the difference between distance and displacement. It's a classic exam question and comes up all the time.

Acceleration

(1) **a** **Label each of the following velocity–time graphs with one of the following.** (3 marks, ★★★)

constant speed	acceleration	deceleration

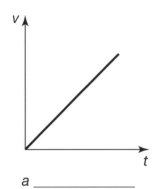

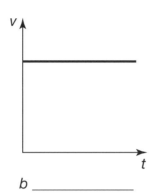

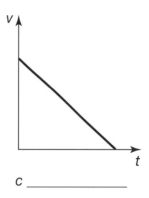

a _____

b _____

c _____

(2) **A car goes on a journey and the velocity–time graph below is made of a short part of the journey. Use the graph to answer the following questions.**

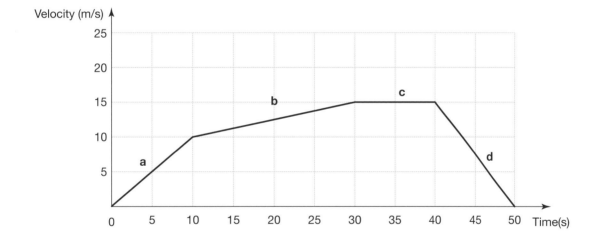

a **Calculate the acceleration during part a.** (2 marks, ★★)

....

....

....

b Calculate the acceleration during part b. (3 marks, ★★★★)

....

....

....

c Describe the car's motion in part c. (1 mark, ★★★★)

....

....

(3) **Using the graph in question 2, calculate the distance travelled during parts a and b of the journey.** (3 marks, ★★★★)

....

....

....

....

NAILIT!

In circular motion such as the Moon orbiting the Earth, the speed of the Moon is constant, but because its direction is constantly changing, its velocity is also constantly changing. This results in an acceleration, which acts towards the Earth. This acceleration is a centripetal or 'centre-seeking' acceleration.

Equations of motion

These equations will be used in the following questions.

- final velocity = initial velocity + acceleration × time ($v = u + at$)

- distance = $\frac{1}{2}$ (initial velocity + final velocity) × time ($s = \frac{1}{2}(u + v)t$)

- (final velocity)^2 = (initial velocity)^2 + 2 × acceleration × distance ($v^2 = u^2 + 2as$)

- distance = initial velocity × time + $\frac{1}{2}$ × acceleration × time^2 ($s = ut + \frac{1}{2}at^2$)

The equations apply for motion with constant acceleration.

They are sometimes referred to as the **SUVAT** equations.

> **DO IT!**
>
> Learn what the letters of **S U V A T** stand for. Keep writing them down and testing yourself until you know them off by heart.

1. **A sports car accelerates from 0 m/s to 50 m/s in 7 seconds on a race track.**

   a **Calculate its acceleration.** (3 marks, ★★★)

   ....

   ....

   A cheetah is watching a gazelle and walking slowly and quietly through a bush.

   Suddenly the cheetah accelerates from 2 m/s to 35 m/s. This takes 3 seconds.

   b **Calculate the acceleration of the cheetah.** (3 marks, ★★★)

   ....

   ....

   c **Compare of the acceleration of the cheetah and the sports car. Is anything surprising about the values?** (2 marks, ★★★)

   ....

   ....

   ....

NAILIT!

It is really important that you can rearrange the equations to work out the answers to the problems. Remember to write each stage carefully.

WORKIT!

A car speeds up along a straight race track from rest to 32 m/s in 16 s.

Calculate its acceleration and the distance it moves in this time.

Step 1 Choose the correct equation.

$$a = \frac{v - u}{t}$$

Step 2 Substitute in the values.

$$\frac{32 - 0}{16} = 2 \text{ m/s}$$

Step 3 Choose the c

Step 4 Substitute in the values.

Correct equation.

$$s = ut + 0.5at^2$$

$(0 \times 16) + (0.5 \times 2 \times 16^2) = 256 \text{ m}$ ◄——— Remember the unit.

Note that it may be possible to use a different equation to get the correct answer.

(2) **A train stops at a station. When the train departs it accelerates at 1 m/s² to reach a maximum speed of 60 m/s. The train then maintains this top speed for 1 hour.**

a **Calculate how long it takes the train to reach its top speed.** (3 marks, ★★★★)

....

....

....

(3) **A skateboarder stands at the top of a ramp of length 30 m, and then accelerates down it. At the bottom of the ramp the speed of the skateboarder is 15 m/s.**

a **Calculate the acceleration of the skateboarder on the ramp.** (4 marks, ★★★★)
Use the equation:

$$v^2 = u^2 + 2as$$

....

....

....

b **Calculate the time it takes the skateboarder to reach the bottom of the ramp.**
(3 marks, ★★★★)

....

....

....

Newton's laws of motion

(1) Complete the sentences with the missing words. (3 marks, ★★)

The .... of an object will only change if there is a .... force acting on it.

When a car is at a .... speed the driving force and .... forces of friction and

.... are equal and act in .... directions.

steady	resistive	opposite	resultant	velocity
drag	balanced	high	upthrust	low

(2) State Newton's second law in words. Use an equation in your answer. (4 marks, ★★★★)

....

....

....

....

(3) Newton's first law is sometimes called the law of inertia. Define inertia. (1 mark, ★★★★)

....

....

(4) A boy jumps out of a boat. When he jumps out of the boat he pushes on the boat with a force of 100 N.

a The boat also pushes on the boy. Draw an arrow on the diagram to show the direction and size of this force. (1 mark, ★★★)

....

....

....

← 100 N

b Explain why you chose the value you did as your answer to part a. (2 marks, ★★★)

....

....

c Which of Newton's laws applies in this situation? (1 mark, ★★★★)

....

....

⑤ A 100 kg box has two forces acting on it.

The forces are acting in opposite directions.

10 N acts to the left. 15 N acts to the right.

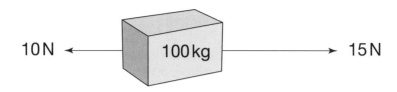

10 N ← 100 kg → 15 N

a **Work out the resultant force on the box.** (1 mark, ★★)

....

....

b **The box was initially at rest. Which way will it move?** (1 mark, ★★)

....

c **Calculate the acceleration of the box.** (3 marks, ★★★★)

....

....

....

WORKIT!

A car of mass 1200 kg accelerates from rest to 20 m/s in 10 s.

a Calculate the car's acceleration. (2 marks, ★★★)

$$a = \frac{v - u}{t}$$

Choose the correct equation and substitute in the values from the question.

$$a = \frac{20 - 0}{10} \quad (1)$$

Remember, from rest means 0 m/s.

$$a = 2 \text{ m/s}^2 \quad (1)$$

Remember to state your answer in the correct units.

b Calculate the resultant force acting on the car. (2 marks, ★★★)

$$F = ma$$

$$F = 1200 \times 2 \quad (1)$$

$$F = 2400 \text{ N} \quad (1)$$

6 A car has a mass of 800 kg and is travelling at a constant speed of 30 m/s.

a **State the resultant force acting on the car.** (1 mark, ★★★)

....

The driver applies the brakes and the braking force is 8000 N.

b **Calculate the deceleration of the car.** (2 marks, ★★★)

....

....

....

c **How long would it take the car to stop?** (3 marks, ★★★★)

....

....

....

NAILIT!

Newton's third law is the best known law, but probably the least understood. Remember the forces act in pairs but **never cancel each other out**. They are the same type of force but act on different objects.

DOIT!

Make sure you learn each of Newton's three laws. The basic idea of each law is actually very simple.

Stopping distance

① **Complete the following equation.** (2 marks, ★★★)

Stopping distance = ... + ...

② **The following graph shows how braking distance and thinking distance are affected by speed.**

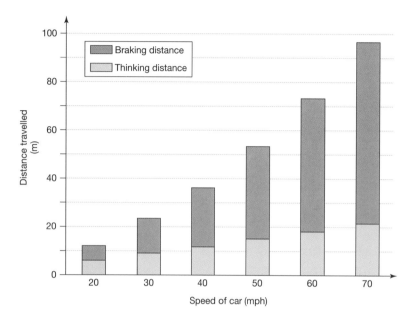

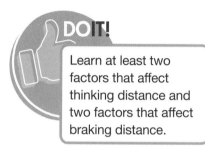

DO IT!

Learn at least two factors that affect thinking distance and two factors that affect braking distance.

a **State two other factors that affect braking distance.** (1 mark, ★★)

....

b **i** **Using the graph, describe the relationship between thinking distance and speed.**
(1 mark, ★★★)

....

ii **Using the graph, describe the relationship between braking distance and speed.**
(2 marks, ★★★★)

....

....

(3) **A student explains a simple experiment to compare the reaction times of different students in her class.**

One student drops the ruler.

The other student has to catch it as quickly as possible.

The shorter the distance that the ruler falls through the fingers, the shorter the reaction time of the student. Repeat the experiment twice and take an average.

Another student says: 'This experiment could be changed to see if texting on a mobile phone affects reaction time'. Explain how this new experiment would be conducted.

(6 marks, ★★★)

....

....

....

....

....

....

NAILIT!

Remember the thinking distance is equal to the speed of the vehicle multiplied by the reaction time of the driver. This is why thinking distance is proportional to speed. The braking distance is linked to kinetic energy, so is proportional to the square of the speed. For example, if speed doubles then the braking distance goes up by four times and if speed triples then braking distance goes up nine-fold. This explains why braking distance goes up so much at higher speeds.

Momentum (1)

(1) **Which of the following is the unit for momentum?** (1 mark, ★★)

m/s
kg m/s
kg/ms
m/s²

(2) **State the formula for momentum.** (1 mark, ★★)

....

(3) **A 1000 kg car is driving along a racing track with a velocity of 400 m/s.**

Calculate its momentum. (3 marks, ★★★)

....

....

....

(4) **A 3500 g labrador is running at 10 m/s.**

Calculate the dog's momentum. (4 marks, ★★★★)

....

....

NAILIT!

Momentum has two units. Make sure you learn them both so you don't get caught out in exams.

NAILIT!

Momentum is a vector, so it has both magnitude and direction.

Momentum (2)

(1) **Complete the following sentence with the missing words.** (2 marks, ★★★)

In a .... system (in which no .... forces act) the total momentum before an event

is equal to the total momentum after the event. This is called the .... of .... law.

external	moments	momentum	conservation
internal	closed	released	sum

(2) **A speeding truck is approaching a stationary car at traffic lights.**

a **Calculate the momentum of the truck.** (2 marks, ★★★)

....

....

b **In an inelastic collision the two vehicles crumple together.**

Calculate the velocity of the truck and car as they move off joined together. (3 marks, ★★★★)

....

....

....

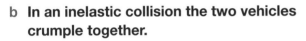

40 m/s →

0 m/s

Truck 2000 kg

Car 800 kg

(3) **Two cars have a head-on collision, their speeds and mass are shown in the diagram. Assume momentum is conserved in the collision.**

Both cars crumple together in an inelastic collision.

Calculate the velocity and direction of the cars as they move off together. (6 marks, ★★★★★)

....

....

....

40 m/s →   ← 30 m/s

800 kg   1000 kg

 **NAILIT!**

When a force acts on an object that is moving, or able to move, a change in momentum occurs.

 **DOIT!**

Make sure that you are confident with collision, recoil and explosion questions.

Momentum (3)

① **Explain, using physics ideas, why a crumple zone may prevent the driver in an accident from being killed during a collision.** (6 marks, ★★★★★)

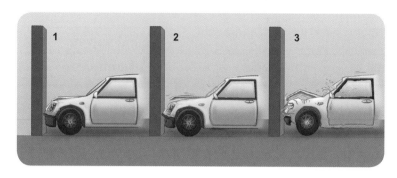

....

....

....

② **A cricket ball of mass 200g is struck with a force of 180N for a period of 0.005s.**

Calculate the change in momentum. (3 marks, ★★★)

....

....

③ **A golf ball of mass 50g is struck with a force of 200N for a period of 0.005s. Calculate:**

a **The change in momentum.** (2 marks, ★★★)

....

....

....

b **The speed of the golf ball immediately afterwards.** (3 marks, ★★★★)

....

....

....

NAILIT!

$F = \dfrac{m\Delta v}{\Delta t}$ is an important equation. It helps us to understand why increasing the time of impact by using crumple zones, for example, can reduce the forces suffered by the driver or passenger in a car collision.

DOIT!

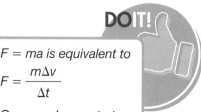

$F = ma$ is equivalent to

$$F = \dfrac{m\Delta v}{\Delta t}$$

Can you demonstrate how?

Waves

Transverse and longitudinal waves

(1) **Water ripples on a surface of a lake are an example of which type of wave?** (1 mark, ★★)

Longitudinal	
Transverse	

EM waves	
Rarefaction	

(2) a **What is a longitudinal wave?** (2 marks, ★★★)

....

....

b **Give an example of a longitudinal wave.** (1 mark, ★★)

....

....

c **Draw a diagram of a longitudinal wave.** (2 marks, ★★★)

(3) **A student is interested in waves.**

She takes a slinky and shakes it up and down while a classmate is holding the other end.

She observes this:

Vibration of coils

Direction of wave

a **What type of wave does she observe? Explain your answer.** (3 marks, ★★★)

....

....

b **What could she do with the slinky to make a different type of wave?** (2 marks, ★★★)

....

....

c **Compare the two wave types. State their differences.** (2 marks, ★★★★)

....

....

DO IT!

Learn at least two examples of each type of wave.

NAILIT!

Waves can be either longitudinal or transverse. Make sure that you know the differences between them.

Properties of waves

(1) **Define the following:**

  a **Amplitude** (2 marks, ★★★)

....

....

  b **Frequency** (2 marks, ★★★)

....

....

  c **Wavelength** (2 marks, ★★★)

....

....

> **DO IT!**
>
> Make flashcards to learn the definitions for **amplitude**, **wavelength**, **frequency** and **time period**.

(2) **The figure below shows an oscilloscope trace of a musical note.**

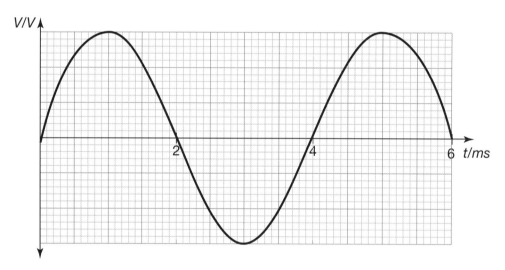

Work out the following:

  a **The time period of the wave.** (2 marks, ★★★)

....

  b **The frequency of the wave.** (2 marks, ★★★)

....

  c **The amplitude of the wave. Each cm square represents 1 V.** (2 marks, ★★★)

....

③ **All EM waves travel at 300 000 000 m/s. BBC Radio 4 broadcasts at a frequency of 603 kHz.**

Calculate the wavelength of the radio wave. (4 marks, ★★★★)

....

....

....

....

NAILIT!

Make sure that you know how to label wavelength and amplitude on a wave diagram.

Watch out for prefixes and powers. Remember that 1 MHz means 1 megahertz. This means 1 million hertz or 1 000 000 Hz.

WORKIT!

a Calculate the period of a radio wave that has a speed of 300 000 000 m/s and frequency of 1 MHz. (2 marks, ★★★)

Step 1 You do not have to use the wave equation, but you will instead need the following equation provided on the physics equation sheet:

$$\text{frequency} = \frac{1}{\text{time period}} = \frac{1}{T} (1)$$

Step 2 Rearrange and then substitute into the equation

$$T = \frac{1}{f} = \frac{1}{1\,000\,000}$$

$$= 1 \times 10^{-6} \text{ s } (1)$$

You can leave the number in standard form as it is very small, otherwise it is 0.000001 s.

b Calculate the wavelength of the radio wave. (1 mark, ★★)

Use formula $v = f \times \lambda$ and rearrange:

$$\lambda = \frac{v}{f} = \frac{3 \times 10^8}{1 \times 10^6}$$

$$= \frac{300\,000\,000}{1\,000\,000}$$

$$= 300 \text{ m } (1)$$

Reflection and refraction

(1) **A wave approaches a boundary. Which three things could happen?** (3 marks, ★★★★)

....

....

....

(2) **The diagram below shows a wave front approaching a hard flat surface.**

Complete the diagram to show reflection taking place. (3 marks, ★★★)

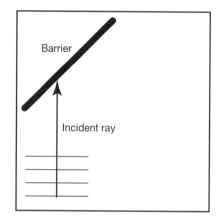

Barrier

Incident ray

(3) **The light ray is moving from air into glass blocks a and b.**

Assume no reflection takes place.

Complete the path of the light rays:

  i **entering**

 ii **travelling through**

iii **leaving the glass blocks**

On each diagram label the normal and direction of the rays.

a (3 marks, ★★★)

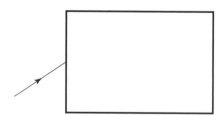

b (3 marks, ★★★★)

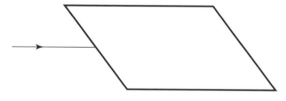

NAILIT!

Remember to add a normal when drawing ray diagrams.

If the wave is travelling from a less dense medium into a denser medium, it slows down and bends towards the normal. If it travels from a denser to less dense medium, it speeds up and bends away from the normal.

DOIT!

Practise drawing diagrams of wave fronts being reflected or refracted at the boundary between two different materials. Always use a ruler!

Sound waves (1)

1. **What is the normal audible frequency range for humans?** (2 marks, ★★★)

....

....

2. **A loudspeaker plays music. The sound waves reach the outer ear.**

   With reference to the diagram to the right, explain how a human can 'hear' music.

   (6 marks, ★★★★)

   The ossicles

   'Hammer'   'Anvil'   'Stirrup'

   Cochlea

   Nerve to brain

   Ear drum

   Oval window

   ....

   ....

   ....

   ....

3. **A tuning fork is struck against a microphone connected to an oscilloscope.**

   The sound wave can be seen on an oscilloscope screen.

   Each horizontal square on the oscilloscope trace represents 1 ms.

   Each vertical square represents 1 V.

   Oscilloscope trace

   a **What is the time period of the wave?** (2 marks, ★★★★)

   ....

   b **Calculate the frequency of the wave.** (2 marks, ★★★)

   ....

   c **What is the amplitude of the wave?** (2 marks, ★★★★)

   ....

DO IT!

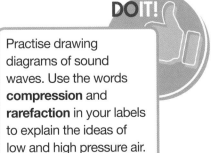

Practise drawing diagrams of sound waves. Use the words **compression** and **rarefaction** in your labels to explain the ideas of low and high pressure air. Label the wavelengths.

NAIL IT!

Sound behaves in a similar way to other mechanical waves. The wave transfers energy through matter such as solids, liquids and gases. The matter vibrates but does not actually move from one place to another.

For example, a wave travelling in water moves from one place to another, but the water doesn't. Each point on the water wave moves up and down perpendicularly to the direction of the wave.

Sound waves (2)

① **Define the term 'ultrasound'.** (2 marks, ★★★)

....

....

② **State two uses or applications of ultrasonic waves.** (2 marks, ★★★)

....

....

③ **Seismograph stations all over the world can detect P-waves and S-waves in the event of an earthquake.**

The diagram below shows the epicentre of an earthquake and the detection of P-waves and S-waves at different seismograph stations locations around the world.

Epicentre

1

2

3

4

→ P- and S-waves

→ P-waves only

a

b

a What is a P-wave? What type of wave is it?
(4 marks, ★★★)

....

....

b What is an S-wave? Describe what type of wave an S-wave is. (4 marks, ★★★)

....

....

DO IT!

Make sure you know the difference between a P-wave and an S-wave. Which is transverse and which is longitudinal?

c Explain why the waves that reach points 1, 2, 3 and 4 curve gradually as they pass through the Earth. (4 marks, ★★★★)

....

....

....

d Explain why only P-waves can be detected at points a and b. (2 marks, ★★★)

....

....

NAILIT!

Ultrasound can be used to measure distances without having to cut something open. Partial reflections of ultrasound take place at boundaries of different materials. It is possible to use an oscilloscope to work out the time it takes for the pulse reflection to return to the transducer. If the speed of ultrasound is known in the material, then you can calculate the distance to the different boundary. This technique can be used for many applications, for example, finding flaws in metal casings and measuring the size of eyeballs.

Electromagnetic waves (1)

(1) Complete the following table. (6 marks, ★★★)

Type of electromagnetic waves

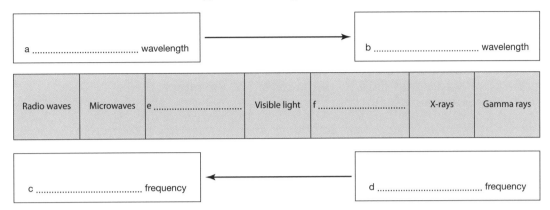

a .... wavelength						b .... wavelength	
Radio waves	Microwaves	e	Visible light	f	X-rays	Gamma rays	

c .... frequency	d .... frequency

(2) State three properties of electromagnetic waves. (3 marks, ★★★)

....

....

(3) Radio waves and microwaves are both used in communications.

Radio waves can be used to transmit television and radio programmes.

Microwaves are used for mobile phones and Wi-Fi.

The different properties of microwaves and radio waves make them suitable for these applications.

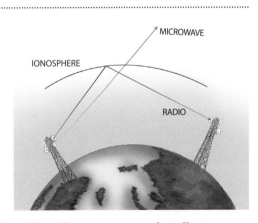

With particular reference to the diagram above, explain why microwaves and radio waves are suitable for these different applications. (6 marks, ★★★★)

....

....

....

....

....

DO IT!

You need to learn the electromagnetic spectrum in the correct order.

Here is a mnemonic:

Red **M**artians **I**nvade **V**enus **U**sing **X**-ray **G**uns

If you don't like it, make up your own one!

NAIL IT!

For waves, wavelength (λ) and frequency (f) are inversely proportional to each other. If the frequency has a very high value, then the wavelength has to be very short.

Electromagnetic waves (2)

1 **Which of the following can be produced by oscillations in electrical circuits?** (2 marks, ★★★★)

Ultraviolet waves		Gamma waves	
Sound waves		Radio waves	

2 **Ultraviolet, X-rays and gamma rays can have hazardous effects on human tissue. Describe two factors that determine the extent of the effect.** (2 marks, ★★★★)

....

....

3 **Match the following EM spectrum waves to the application/use.** (6 marks, ★★★)

1 Radio waves		**a** Fibre optics and communication
2 Microwaves		**b** TV and radio
3 Infrared		**c** Heaters and cooking food
4 Visible light		**d** Sun tanning
5 Ultra violet		**e** Medical imaging and treatments
6 X-rays + gamma rays		**f** Satellite communications and cooking food

NAILIT!

Ultraviolet, X-rays and gamma rays are all ionising radiation. Over-exposure to any of them can lead to gene mutation and cancer.

DOIT!

This is real spider diagram and flashcard territory. It is important that you make an effort to learn at least two uses or applications for each member of the electromagnetic spectrum.

WORKIT!

A radio wave passes into a metal TV aerial.

Explain what effect the radio wave has on the metal TV aerial. (3 marks, ★★)

Radio waves can be absorbed by the metal TV aerial. (1)

The radio waves may induce an alternating current. (1)

The alternating current has the same frequency as the radio wave that induced it. (1)

Lenses

(1) a **A lens forms an image by refracting light. State the two types of lens.** (2 marks, ★★★)

....

....

b **State the types of images that can be formed by the lenses in part a.** (2 marks, ★★★)

....

....

....

(2) **Complete and annotate the diagrams below using the following labels:** (6 marks, ★★★)

convex	concave	parallel	light	rays
principal	focus	focal		length

a

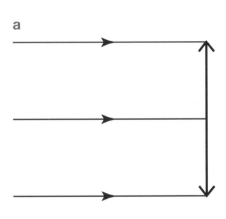

b

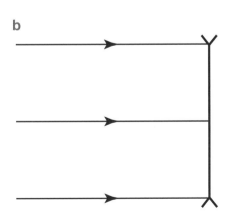

③ a Complete the ray diagram below to show the image formed by the lens. (6 marks, ★★★★)

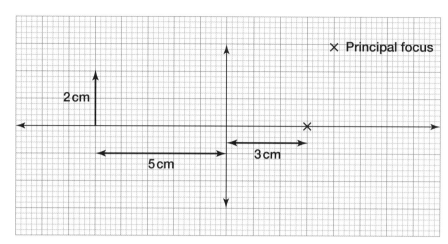

b State the type of image formed. (1 mark, ★★★)

....

....

c Calculate the magnification of the image formed. (2 marks, ★★★)

....

....

....

....

....

NAILIT!

Magnification is a ratio and does not have units.

DOIT!

Make sure you learn the two lens types in ray diagrams.

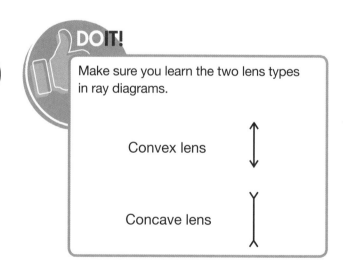

Visible light

(1) **Label the two types of reflection in the diagrams below.** (2 marks, ★★★)

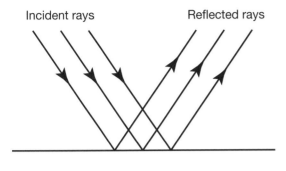

Incident rays   Reflected rays

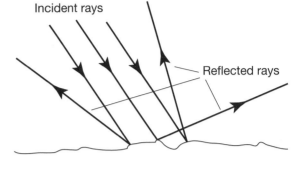

Incident rays

Reflected rays

a .... **reflection**   b .... **reflection**

(2) **Complete the missing words in the sentences below.**

a **Objects that transmit light are either** .... **or** .... **.** (2 marks, ★★★)

b **The colour of an object that we observe is related to the different amounts of**

........................., ... **and** .... **of different wavelengths of light by**

the object. (3 marks, ★★★)

c .... **objects absorb or reflect the majority of the light incident on**

them. (1 mark, ★★★)

NAILIT!

Remember that a filter will absorb certain wavelengths of light (or colours) and will transmit certain wavelengths of light (or colours). A cyan filter, for example, will transmit green and blue light, but would absorb red light.

DOIT!

Learn the three primary colours for light and make sure you know all the different combinations. What combinations make magenta, cyan and yellow?

③ **A student considers the effect that using filters has on the colour of objects she observes.**

She shines white light from a torch. First the white light passes through a magenta filter and then the light passes through a red filter.

Then the student observes what colour some red poppies appear when the filtered light is shone on it.

The experimental set-up can be seen in the diagram below.

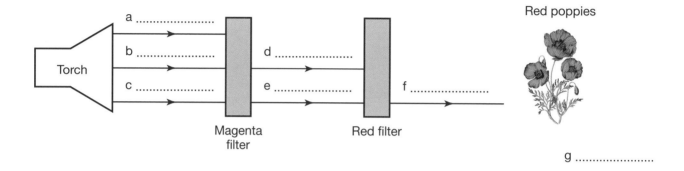

Label:

i **The missing primary colours on a, b and c that make up white light.** (3 marks, ★★★)

ii **The 2 primary colours on d and e transmitted by the magenta filter.** (2 marks, ★★★)

iii **The primary colour transmitted by the red filter.** (1 mark, ★★★)

iv **The colour that the red poppies will appear to the student on g.** (1 mark, ★★★)

Emission and absorption of infrared radiation and black body radiation

1. **If an object radiates and absorbs radiation at the same rate what does this tell you about the object's temperature?** (1 mark, ★★★)

It is increasing			It is constant	
It is decreasing			It is impossible to know	

2. **A student carries out an experiment on the absorption and emission of infrared radiation.**

He paints one can white and another black.

He then fills them both with the same amount of boiling water.

He records the temperature change with a thermometer for each can 15 minutes later.

The student records that the black can's temperature goes down by 15°C, but the white can's temperature goes down by only 5°C. **Explain why.** (3 marks, ★★★★)

....

....

....

....

....

③ The student modifies the experiment and places an infrared heater equally spaced from both cans. He then fills both cans with cold water. He turns on the heater and records the temperature change after 15 minutes.

a Would the temperature of the water in each can increase or decrease by the same amount? Explain your answer. (3 marks, ★★★★)

....

....

....

....

....

b Describe the limitations of the experiment. (3 marks, ★★★)

....

....

....

....

WORKIT!

The student was only interested in finding out about absorption and emission of infrared radiation. What other factors may have affected his experiment? (1 mark, ★★)

The experiment will also be affected by conduction and convection. (1)

④ An object has an increasing temperature. Which of the following statements is true? (1 mark, ★)

Absorption and emission of infrared are at the same rate	
Absorption and emission of infrared are at different rates	
Absorption of infrared is greater than emission of infrared	
Emission of infrared is great than absorption of infrared	

5 The following graph shows the continuous spectra for stars that have different surface temperatures. The surface temperatures are given in kelvin (K).

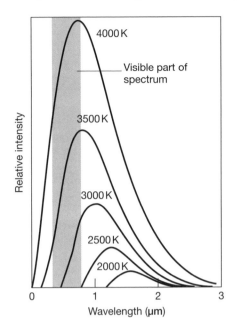

a Each star has a peak wavelength. Define peak wavelength. (2 marks, ★★★★)

....

....

b State the relationship between the temperature of a star and the peak wavelength.
(2 marks, ★★★★)

....

....

6 Explain the factors that determine the temperature of the Earth. (6 marks, ★★★★)

....

....

....

....

....

....

DO IT!

Learn the definition for a perfect black body.

'A perfect black body is an object that absorbs all of the radiation incident on it'

NAIL IT!

All objects emit infrared radiation, the hotter the object the more radiation it emits.

Magnetism

① **Complete the sentence. The poles of a magnet are the places where:** (1 mark, ★★)

the magnetic fields are the strongest	
the field lines are the furthest apart	
the magnetic fields are the weakest	
flux lines overlap	

> **NAILIT!**
>
> Make sure you learn that magnetic materials are iron, steel, cobalt and nickel.

② a **What is an induced magnet?** (2 marks, ★★★)

....

....

b **What kind of force always exists between a permanent and an induced magnet?** (1 mark, ★★★)

....

c **Describe a simple test to check if a material is an induced or permanent magnet.** (3 marks, ★★★★)

....

....

....

③ **Draw the field lines on the following magnet combinations.** (6 marks, ★★★★)

a b

> **DOIT!**
>
> The direction of a magnetic field at any point is given by the direction of the force that would act on another north pole placed at that point. Remember north pole really means north-seeking pole.

Electromagnetism

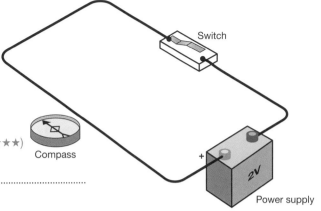

① A student builds the circuit to the right. The circuit contains a dc power supply and a switch. He places a plotting compass near the wire.

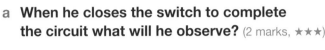

Compass

2V

Power supply

a When he closes the switch to complete the circuit what will he observe? (2 marks, ★★★)

....

....

b The student reverses the battery connection then closes the switch. What will he observe now? (2 mark, ★★★)

....

....

② The diagrams show a wire carrying current in the direction indicated by the arrow.

For each wire sketch the magnetic field that would be induced.
(6 marks, ★★★★)

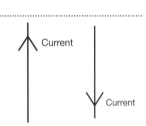

Current

Current

③ A current-carrying wire is placed between the two magnets below.

The current direction is indicated with an arrow.

a Draw an arrow on the wire to show the direction in which it will experience a force. (1 mark, ★★★★)

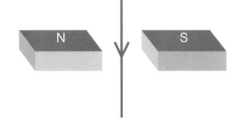

b What is the name given to this effect? (1 mark, ★★★★)

....

c What changes could be made to make the wire move with a greater force?
(3 marks, ★★★★)

....

....

NAILIT!

A wire shaped into a coil that carries a current is called a solenoid. A solenoid has the same magnetic field pattern as a bar magnet. The field inside a solenoid is strong and uniform (that is, the field lines are parallel and the same distance away from each other).
If you place a core inside the solenoid, you have created an electromagnet.

Motor effect

(1) **Add the following labels to the electric motor diagram below. Some labels are used more than once.** (6 marks, ★★★★)

| force | split-ring-commutator | rotating coil | dc power supply | brush |

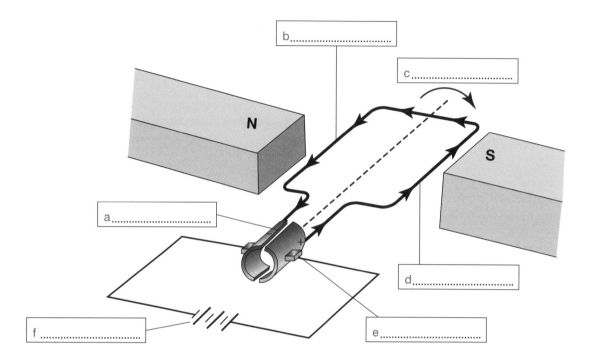

(2) **a Explain the function of a split-ring commutator in a dc motor.** (2 marks, ★★★★)

....

....

b Explain the role of the brushes in an electric motor. (2 marks, ★★★★)

....

....

NAILIT!

Learn the different parts of the dc motor. Make sure you know the difference between a split-ring commutator and slip rings. Do you know why a split-ring commutator is used in a dc motor?

NAILIT!

Learn Fleming's left-hand rule. It comes up all the time. Remember that the left-hand rule is for motors.

(3) **The diagram below shows a student's design for a loudspeaker.**

The student will plug his MP3 player into the loudspeaker.

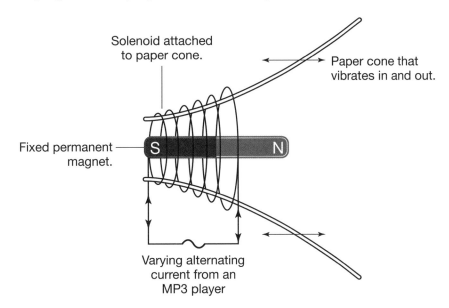

Solenoid attached to paper cone.

Paper cone that vibrates in and out.

Fixed permanent magnet.

S   N

Varying alternating current from an MP3 player

With reference to the diagram, explain how the loudspeaker converts an electrical signal into sound waves. (6 marks, ★★★★)

....

....

....

....

....

....

....

NAILIT!

A loudspeaker uses the motor effect to convert variations in the current to the pressure variations in sound waves.
You need to be able to explain how a loudspeaker works.
Remember to use bullet points and explain it stage by stage.

Electromagnetic induction

(1) **Are the following statements true (T) or false (F)? Circle the correct answer.** (4 marks, ★★★)

a If a conductor moves at an angle to a magnetic field a potential difference   T   F
is not induced in the conductor.

b If a potential difference is induced across the ends of a conductor, a current   T   F
always flows.

c The left-hand rule is used for the motor effect and right-hand rule for the   T   F
generator effect.

d The generator effect can be used in a generator and a dynamo to generate ac.   T   F

(2) **A student moves a metal conducting rod between the poles of a horseshoe magnet.**

Both sides of the rod are connected to a very sensitive ammeter (or galvanometer).

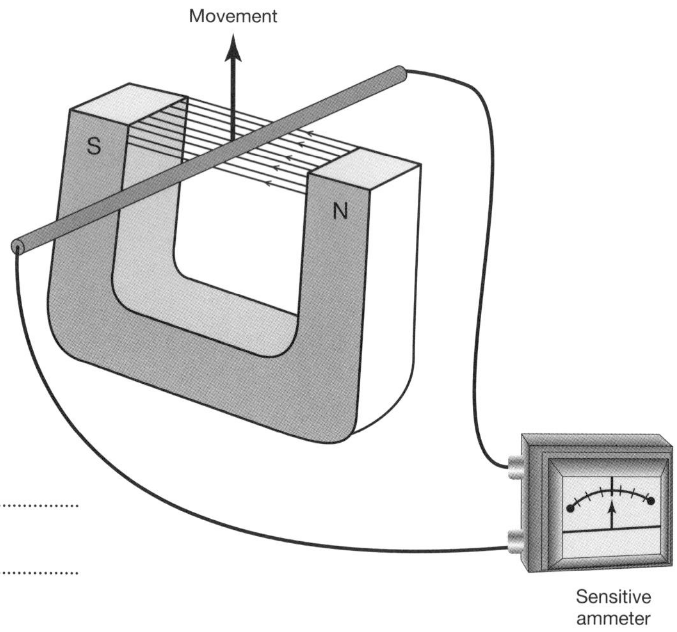

Movement

S

N

Sensitive
ammeter

a If she moves the rod up through the field between the poles as shown in the diagram what will she observe?
(2 marks, ★★★★)

....

....

....

b State the name of the phenomenon she observed in part a. Explain why it happens.
(3 marks, ★★★★)

....

....

....

c What will happen if she moves the rod down between the poles instead of up?
(2 marks, ★★★★)

....

....

....

d **What will happen if she moves the rod up and down between the poles at a steady speed?** (3 marks, ★★★)

....

....

....

(3) **A boy has a dynamo on his bike. He connects it to a light bulb. When he cycles, the magnet rotates and the bulb lights up.**

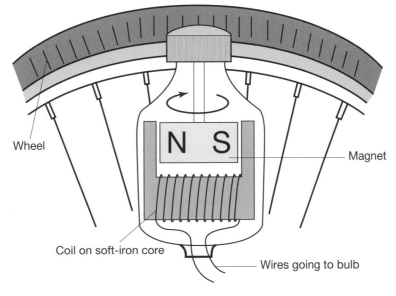

Wheel

N S

Magnet

Coil on soft-iron core

Wires going to bulb

a **Explain why this happens.** (4 marks, ★★★★)

....

....

....

....

b **Why do you think dynamos are no longer legal on UK roads at night?** (2 marks, ★★★★)

....

....

....

NAILIT!

If you move a magnet into a coil, it will induce a current. The current flow will have an associated magnetic field that opposes the magnet's motion. For example, if you push a north pole into the coil, the coil's magnetic field will also be north. What will happen to the coil's field when you pull out the north pole?

DOIT!

You need to learn that if you double the speed of a coil in a magnetic field, not only will the frequency of the induced voltage double, but its amplitude will also double.

Transformers

(1) The diagram to the right shows an old-fashioned carbon microphone.

If the carbon powder is compressed by pressure, its resistance changes.

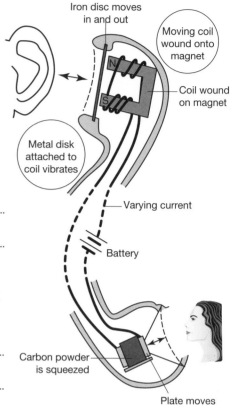

a With reference to the diagram, explain why the current changes when a person talks into the microphone. (3 marks, ★★★★)

....

....

b With reference to the diagram, explain why a changing current makes the metal plate vibrate back and forth. (3 marks, ★★★★)

....

....

....

c With reference to the diagram, explain why the coil is wound onto a magnet. (2 marks, ★★★)

....

(2) The following diagram shows a transformer.

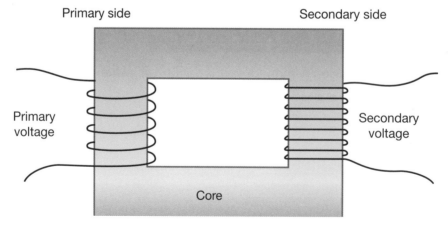

What type of transformer is shown in the diagram? Explain your answer. (2 marks, ★★★)

....

....

(3) **Transformers are used in ac transmission.**

a **Explain how a transformer works.** (6 marks, ★★★★)

....

....

....

....

....

b **Explain why a transformer can only be used with ac, and not dc.** (3 marks, ★★★)

....

....

....

WORKIT!

A transformer is used in a laboratory. The voltage input to the primary coil is 230 V.

The primary coil has 200 turns and the secondary coil has 1000 turns.

a Calculate the potential difference output of the secondary coil. (2 marks, ★★★)

$$\frac{V_P}{V_s} = \frac{n_P}{n_s}$$ ← Choose the correct equation

$$\frac{230}{V_s} = \frac{200}{1000} \rightarrow V_s = \frac{230 \times 1000}{200} = 1150 \ (1)$$ ← Substitute in the values

Express answer with correct units Vs = 1150V (1)

b If current in the primary is 3A calculate the current in the secondary coil. Assume the transformer is 100% efficient. (2 marks, ★★★)

$$V_s I_s = V_P I_P \rightarrow 1150 \times I_s = 230 \times 3 \ (1)$$ ← Remember to select the right equation and substitute in the values

$$I_s = \frac{230 \times 3}{1150}$$

$$= 0.6 A \ (1)$$

c Explain why this current would be more suitable for transmission. (1 mark, ★★★)

Current is lower, so power losses would be lower. (1)

NAILIT!

Make sure that you know how to rearrange the transformer equations.

$$\frac{V_p}{V_s} = \frac{n_p}{n_s}$$

NAILIT!

Remember that transformers only work with ac. Transformers are very useful because when potential difference is stepped up, the current goes down. This can be explained with this formula: $V_s I_s = V_p I_p$. This means that there are less power losses in transmission. (This can be explained with the formula $P = I^2 R$.)

Our solar system

(1) **Which galaxy is the Earth part of? Circle the correct answer.** (1 mark, ★★)

The solar system	The Milky Way	Andromeda	Orion's Belt

(2) a **Fill in the gaps to provide a list of the planets of the solar system.** (4 marks, ★★)

Mercury		Earth		Jupiter		Uranus	

b **Why isn't Pluto included in the list above?** (2 marks, ★★★)

....

....

c **What is another name for the natural satellite of a planet?** (1 mark, ★★★)

....

d **What is the name of the nearest star to the Earth?** (1 mark, ★★)

....

(3) a **Rank the following in order of size from 1 (smallest) to 7 (largest).** (6 marks, ★★★)

Planet	Moon	Dwarf planet	Solar system	Sun	Universe	Galaxy
	1					

NAILIT!

Learn the difference between polar and geostationary satellites. Geostationary satellites stay in a fixed position above the Earth and orbit at the same speed as the Earth. Polar satellites orbit around the poles and the Earth spins under them, so they get to see much more of the Earth.

WORKIT!

a Define the term nebula. (1 mark, ★★)

A nebula is a cloud of dust and gas. (1) ←

> Remember to include the keywords to hoover up those marks.

b How does a nebula go on to form a star? (4 marks, ★★)

Gravity pulls together the dust and gas in the nebula. (1) ←

> Structure your answer in short sentences, this will make it easier for the person marking it.

When pressure and temperature are high enough, fusion takes place. (1)

Outward pressure due to fusion energy is balanced by inward gravitational force. (1)

Stars remain in this stable state of equilibrium for a very long time (millions to billions of years). (1)

DOIT!

Learn the order of the planets. Try using a mnemonic. Here is an example: my very easy method just speeds up naming (planets). Make sure you also know how ideas about our solar system have evolved over the last few hundred years.

Life cycle of a star

(1) **Complete the following sentences with the missing words.** (6 marks, ★★★)

When a star is a main-sequence star, this means the inward force of ....

is balanced with the outward radiation pressure caused by ....

This state of .... can last for millions to billions of years depending

on the star's .... When a star similar in size to our own runs out of

.... it grows in size and becomes a ....

| red giant | equilibrium | hydrogen | fusion | neutron |
| stable | mass | supernova | white | dwarf | gravity |

(2) **The following flow chart is a summary of the life cycle of stars. Complete the missing labels a–f in the flow chart.** (6 marks, ★★★★)

NAILIT!

There are three main paths of the life cycle of a star you need to learn:

1 Stars of a similar size to our Sun
2 Stars bigger than our Sun
3 Stars much bigger than our Sun

The beginning of each cycle is the same but the fate of the star is different in each of the three paths.

Nebula

a

Main sequence star

Small stars

Massive stars

b

c

White dwarf

Supernova

d

e

f

(3) **The universe contains an abundance of elements. Explain which stages of the life cycle of stars have made this possible.** (6 marks, ★★★★)

DOIT!

Practise drawing flow charts or spider diagrams of the life cycle of stars.

....

....

....

....

....

Orbital motion, natural and artificial satellites

(1) Circle the force that allows planets and satellites to maintain their circular orbits.

(1 mark, ★★)

| Centrifugal forces | Circular forces | Planet and satellite forces | Gravity |

(2) Describe the differences and similarities between natural and artificial satellites.

(4 marks, ★★★)

....

....

....

DO IT!

Make sure you learn the difference between an artificial and natural satellite and learn the correct meaning of the word moon. This word doesn't just belong to our Moon!

(3) The following diagram shows the path of Halley's Comet.

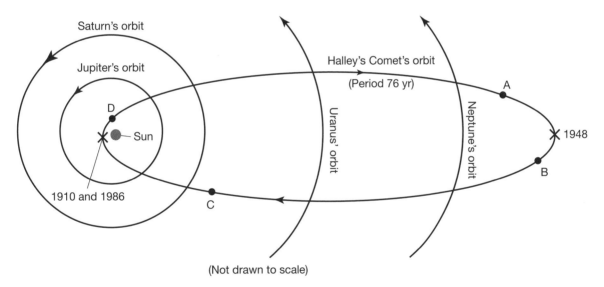

(Not drawn to scale)

a What does period mean in this diagram? (1 mark, ★★★)

....

b What happens to the speed of the comet when it gets close to the Sun? Explain your answer. (2 marks, ★★★)

....

....

④ **Venus is the planet in our solar system with the most circular orbit.**

Venus' orbital speed is constant, but its velocity is constantly changing. Explain how this is possible. (3 marks, ★★★★)

....

....

....

⑤ **Jupiter's orbit is not circular, it is elliptical. This means it is not a perfect circle.**

a **Describe Jupiter's distance from the Sun.** (1 mark, ★★★★)

....

....

b **What effect, if any, will this have on the orbital speed of Jupiter? Explain your answer.** (2 marks, ★★★★)

....

....

NAILIT!

Very few planets (if any) have a perfectly circular orbit. Most of them have an elliptical orbit. This is elongated and looks a bit like an egg.

Red-shift

(1) **a What does the Big Bang theory suggest about the beginning of the universe?**
(2 marks, ★★★)

....

....

....

b Which observations from 1998 onwards have provided evidence to support the Big Bang theory? (1 mark, ★★★)

....

....

(2) **The diagram shows emission spectra from two galaxies of approximately the same size and similar average temperature.**

Emission spectra from a nearby galaxy

Short wavelength ——————————————→ Long wavelength

Emission spectra from a distant galaxy

a What observation can be made about the emission spectra from the distant galaxy?
(2 marks, ★★★)

....

....

b What does this observation reveal about the motion of the distant galaxy? (2 marks, ★★★)

....

....

c How does the observation support the Big Bang theory? (2 marks, ★★★)

....

....

....

(3) **The Big Bang theory does not provide information for two big unanswered questions in physics.**

These are:

- **Why is the rate of expansion of the universe increasing?**

- **Why does the universe have more mass than simply the sum of the mass of suns, planets, and other stellar material?**

State the two hypotheses that have been put forward by the scientific community to answer these questions. (2 marks, ★★★★)

a ....

....

b ....

....

NAILIT!

Make an effort to read up on the alternative theories to the Big Bang theory. The most popular one was the Steady State theory. This stated that the universe was eternal and had no beginning and galaxies were born from white holes. Like the Big Bang, the Steady State theory still had an expanding universe, but the discovery of cosmic microwave background radiation was the nail in the coffin of this theory!

DOIT!

We observe a similar effect to red-shift with sound. It is called the **Doppler effect**. If a car moves towards us, the sound waves get squashed together (making it high pitched). As it moves away, the sound waves get stretched out (making it low pitched). Watch a professional car race for a few minutes and you will hear this.

1.1 a State the formula for calculating the kinetic energy of a moving object. (1 mark)

....

A dog is chasing a cat in a field. Both the dog and cat are running at a steady speed of 10 m/s. The cat has a mass of 3 kg and the dog has a mass of 8 kg.

b Calculate the energy in the kinetic store of the cat. (2 marks)

....

....

c Calculate the energy in the kinetic store of the dog. (2 marks)

....

....

d The dog accelerates to a new steady speed and increases the energy in its kinetic store to 576 J. Calculate the dog's new speed. (4 marks)

....

....

....

....

e The cat maintains the same speed of 10 m/s. The cat is 10 metres ahead of the dog. Calculate the time it takes for the dog to catch the cat. (2 marks)

....

....

1.2 **Complete the following with the different energy stores.** (6 marks)

a .... transferred from a torch.

b .... store of a stretched rubber band.

c .... from a singer performing.

d .... energy store of a battery.

e .... store of a moving bus.

f .... store of a boulder on the edge of a cliff.

1.3 **Bradley has a breakfast of porridge followed by eggs.**

Bradley then goes for a bike ride up and then down a hill.

At the bottom of the hill he has to use his brakes to stop.

Use ideas about energy stores and systems to describe his journey. (6 marks)

....

....

....

....

....

....

2.1 a Explain with the use of diagrams the particle arrangements of solids, liquids and gases. (6 marks)

Sometimes models are put forward to describe particle behaviour.

A student has a tray of marbles and wishes to explain ideas about matter and particles.

b Explain what the marbles represent in the student's model. (1 mark)

c The student wishes to use the model to demonstrate a solid. Describe how he could he do this. (1 mark)

d The student wishes to use the model to demonstrate evaporation. Describe how he could do this. (2 marks)

3.1 A student lights a fire lighter and uses it to heat up 0.25 kg of water.

When the fire lighter has all burnt away, the water temperature has increased by 10 °C.

All of the energy in the chemical store of the fire lighter is transferred to the thermal store of the water.

The specific heat capacity of water is: 4200 J/kg °C.

Calculate the (energy) increase in the thermal store of the water in joules. (4 marks)

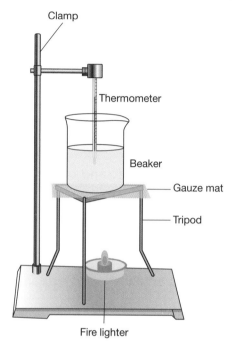

Clamp

Thermometer

Beaker

Gauze mat

Tripod

Fire lighter

....

....

....

....

3.2 Elena climbs up 3 flights of stairs. The total vertical distance she covers is 12 m.

The energy in her gravitational store increases by 6 kJ.

The Earth's gravitational field strength is 10 N/kg.

Calculate Elena's mass. (4 marks)

....

....

....

....

....

4.1 The current in a resistor and then in an unknown component X is measured for different voltages.

The table shows the results.

| Voltage/V | Current/A | |
	Resistor	Component X
1	0.10	0.20
2	0.20	0.40
3	0.30	0.60
4	0.40	0.75
5	0.50	0.80
6	0.60	0.84

a On the grid below and on the same axes, plot graphs of this data for the resistor and component X. Plot voltage on the x-axis and current on the y-axis. (5 marks)

b Draw lines of best fit for the resistor and component X. (2 marks)

c Determine what component X is and justify your choice. (2 marks)

d Use the graph to determine the resistance of the resistor. (2 marks)

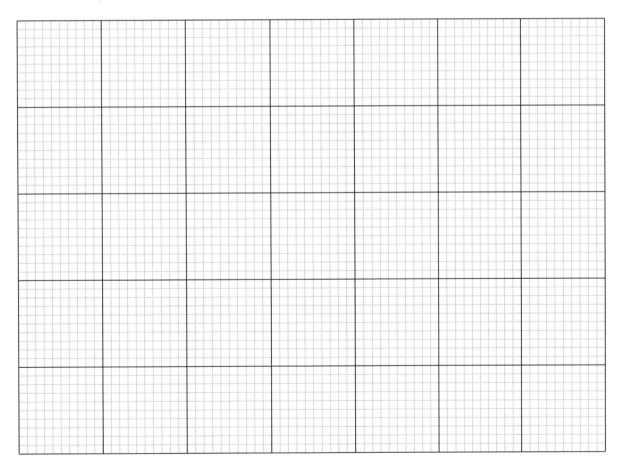

Resistance = _____

5.1 **A carriage containing passengers on a roller coaster is raised through a vertical height of 90 m.**

The combined mass of the carriage and the passengers is 2000 kg.

The Earth's gravitational field strength is 10 N/kg.

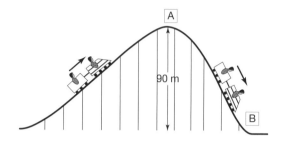

a **The carriage is lifted 90 m vertically to point A on the diagram.**

Calculate the energy increase in the gravitational potential store of the carriage in kJ.
(3 marks)

....

....

....

Increase in gravitational energy store = ... kJ

b **During the ride the carriage drops from point A to point B as shown in the diagram.**

Assume energy is conserved and friction or air resistance acting on the carriage are negligible and can be ignored.

Calculate the speed of the carriage at point B. (5 marks)

....

....

....

....

....

Speed of carriage at point B = ... m/s

6.1 **Americium-241 is used commonly in smoke alarms around the world.**

Americium is an alpha emitter and has a half-life of 433 years.

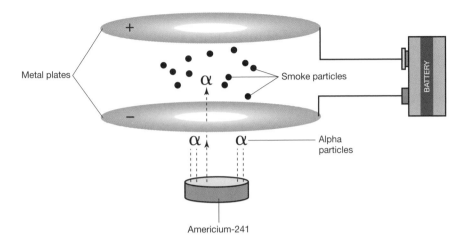

In normal use the alpha particles emitted ionise the air and cause a current to flow.

If the current continues to flow the smoke alarm will not sound.

a **Explain why an alpha emitter is used for this application.** (2 marks)

....

....

b **It is a criminal offence in the UK to tamper with smoke alarms that contain americium-241. Explain why.** (3 marks)

....

....

....

c **The half-life of americium-241 is stated as 433 years. Define the term half-life.** (2 marks)

....

....

....

d Americium is used for the smoke alarm because it has a very long half-life.

Ignoring background radiation, a G–M tube detects a count-rate of 30 counts per minute from the americium-241.

Calculate how many half-lives it would take the americium-241's count-rate to fall to $\frac{1}{4}$ of its original value. (2 marks)

....

....

e How many years is this? (1 mark)

....

6.2 **a** Match the keyword to its definition. (4 marks)

1 Nucleus	**a** An atom with the same number of protons and a different number of neutrons.
2 Isotope	**b** It is only composed of protons and neutrons.
3 Ion	**c** A neutral particle with the same mass as a proton.
4 Neutron	**d** An atom that has lost or gained an electron.

b When a neutron inside a nucleus decays into a proton and emits an electron this is called: (1 mark)

Beta decay	
Gamma decay	
Alpha decay	
Neutron emission	

c An alpha particle is the same as: (1 mark)

A hydrogen atom	
A neutral atom	
Gamma radiation	
A helium nucleus	

7.1 **Explain using the following words what an electric field is and how it affects charged objects placed within it.** (4 marks)

electric	force	repulsive	same
attractive	charged	exerts	opposite

....

....

....

....

8.1 **A teacher carries out a demonstration with protactinium-234 in a laboratory. Protactinium has a half-life of approximately 69 seconds.**

The nuclear equation below shows the changes to the atomic and mass numbers of protactinium when it undergoes decay, and the new element that is formed.

$$^{234}_{91}\text{Pa} \rightarrow {}^{234}_{92}\text{U} + \text{radiation}$$

a **State the type of radiation released in the above nuclear equation.** (1 mark)

....

b **Describe the change that takes place in the protactinium nucleus before this radiation is released.** (3 marks)

....

....

....

c **The teacher wears gloves when handling the protactinium. Describe how this will this protect her.** (1 mark)

....

d **In what way will wearing gloves not protect the teacher? Explain your answer.** (2 mark)

....

....

e **How should the teacher move and store the protactinium once the experiment is over?** (2 marks)

....

....

9.1 **The block in the image below is made of iron and has a mass of 192 g.**

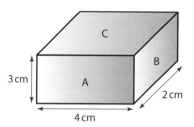

(Not drawn to scale)

a **Calculate the volume of the block in cm³.** (1 mark)

....

b **Calculate the block's density in g/cm³.** (2 marks)

....

....

c **Convert the density value to kg/m³.** (2 marks)

....

....

d **A student picks up the block and presses it down on the table first with face A and then with face B with the same force.**

Explain, without a calculation, which face (A or B) will exert the most pressure on the table. (2 marks)

....

....

e **Calculate the pressure exerted on the table in kilopascals if face A is placed on the table.** (4 marks)

....

....

....

.... kPa

For an additional practice paper, visit: www.scholastic.co.uk/gcse

Energy

Energy stores and systems

1 A system is an object, or group of objects. The **energy** in a system is a numerical **value** that tells us whether certain **changes** in the system could, or could not, happen. The total **amount** of energy in a system is always the **same** no matter what changes happen in the system, but the energy available can be **redistributed** in different parts of this system.

2 3–d; 4–g; 5–e; 6–c; 7– f; 8–a

3 1 – Chemical; 2 – Heating; 3 – Heating; 4 – Thermal; 5 – Thermal.

Changes in energy stores: kinetic energy

1 **a** Kinetic energy = $0.5 \times$ mass $\times$ speed^2 Or $\frac{1}{2}mv^2$

   b J or joules

2 Kinetic energy = $0.5 \times$ mass $\times$ speed^2

   Kinetic energy = $0.5 \times 1\,000 \times 10^2$

   $50\,000\,$J or $50\,$kJ

3 Kinetic energy = $0.5 \times$ mass $\times$ speed^2 rearrange to:

   mass = $\frac{\text{kinetic energy}}{0.5 \times \text{speed}^2}$

   mass = $800\,000 / 0.5 \times 10^2$

   $16\,000\,$kg or $16\,$tonnes

Changes in energy stores: elastic potential energy

1 $E_e = 0.5 \times$ spring constant $\times$ extension^2

   or $E_e = \frac{1}{2}ke^2$.

2 $E_e = 0.5 \times$ spring constant $\times$ extension^2

   Extension = $25 - 5 = 20\,$cm;

   Extension = $0.2\,$m

   $E_e = 0.5 \times 10 \times 0.2^2$

   $E_e = 0.2\,$J

3 $F = ke$, $k = \frac{F}{e} = \frac{2.5}{0.1} = 25\,$N/m

4 $E_e = 0.5 \times$ spring constant $\times$ extension^2 : rearrange to

   extension = $\sqrt{\frac{E_e}{0.5 \times \text{spring constant}}}$

   Extension = $\sqrt{\frac{20\,\text{J}}{0.5 \times 10\,000}}$

   Extension = $0.063\,$m

   convert to cm = $6.3\,$cm

Changes in energy stores: gravitational potential energy

1 $E_p = mgh$ or gravitational potential energy = mass $\times$ gravitational field strength $\times$ height.

2 $E_p = mgh$

   $E_p = 4 \times 10 \times 4$

   $E_p = 160\,$J or joules

3 $E_p = mgh$

   $E_p = 40 \times 10 \times 5$

   $E_p = 2000\,$J or joules

4 $E_p = mgh$ rearrange to:

   $h = \frac{E_p}{m \times g}$; $m = 300\,$g $= 0.3\,$kg

   $h = \frac{90}{0.3 \times 10}$

   $h = 30\,$m

Energy changes in systems: specific heat capacity

1 **a** Specific heat capacity is the amount of energy required to increase the temperature of 1 kg of a substance by 1 °C

   b Change in thermal energy = mass $\times$ specific heat capacity $\times$ temp change or $\Delta E = m \times c \times \Delta\theta$

   c J/kg °C.

2 Copper has a lower specific heat capacity than iron; The same amount of energy is delivered to each block; Copper will require less energy to raise its temperature.

3 $\Delta E = m \times c \times \Delta\theta$ rearrange to:

   $m = \frac{\Delta E}{c \times \Delta\theta}$; Temp change

   $= 35 - 25 = 10\,°$C

   $m = \frac{1500}{2400 \times 10}$

   $m = 0.063\,$kg

Power

1 **a** Bill: $\frac{7500}{60} = 125\,$W;

   $\frac{17\,800}{60} = 297\,$W; $\frac{7200}{60} = 120\,$W

   Ted: $\frac{6300}{60} = 105\,$W;

   $\frac{20\,000}{60} = 333\,$W; $\frac{8040}{60} = 134\,$W

   b Ted; average power = $\frac{105 + 333 + 134}{3} = 191\,$W,

   Bill average power = $\frac{125 + 297 + 120}{3} = 181\,$W

   Therefore Ted is the most powerful.

2 Energy = power $\times$ time

   time = $7.5 \times 60 \times 60 = 27\,000\,$s

   Energy = $50 \times 27\,000$

   Energy = $1.35\,$MJ or $1\,350\,000\,$J

3 Time = $\frac{\text{energy}}{\text{power}}$

   Time = $\frac{2\,200\,000}{100\,000}$

   Time = $22\,$s

Energy transfers in a system

1 Energy stores can neither be created nor destroyed; but can be redistributed to other parts of the system via transfer or dissipation.

2 *Any sensible suggestion*. Battery-powered helicopter; MP3 player; electric fire.

3 **a** Gravitational potential to kinetic

   b Chemical to thermal

   c Elastic potential to kinetic (and thermal and vibrational)

   d Chemical to thermal and kinetic (and vibrational)

Efficiency

1 **a** Efficiency = $\frac{\text{useful output energy transfer}}{\text{total input energy transfer}}$

   b Ratio or percentage

2 Answers in order: initial; final. Gravitational; kinetic, thermal and vibrational. Chemical; kinetic, gravitational potential, thermal and vibrational. Chemical; Chemical, kinetic and vibrational.

3 Efficiency = $\frac{360}{500} = 0.72$ or 72%

4 Efficiency = $\frac{900}{5000} = 0.18$ or 18%

National and global energy resources

1 **a** Renewable: Wave; Solar; Wind; Hydroelectric [Remove 1 mark per incorrect response]

   b Requires burning: Oil and coal (both required)

2 Only renewable if extensive replanting takes place.

3 **a** $15\,$m/s

   b $\frac{\text{Total power output}}{\text{Max turbine power output}} =$

   $\frac{10\,000\,000}{1\,000\,000} = 10$ turbines

   c Wind supply fluctuates, is weather dependent.

4 Advantages: wind is renewable, doesn't emit greenhouse gases.

Disadvantages: wind is unreliable, requires a huge amount of land, is considered an eyesore.

Electricity

Standard circuit diagram symbols

1 Correct drawings of the following:

2 LDR	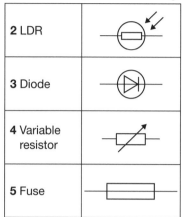
3 Diode	
4 Variable resistor	
5 Fuse	

2 a Diagram includes a battery (or cell), variable resistor, ammeter and bulb connected in series; Voltmeter must be connected in parallel with the bulb.

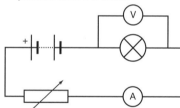

b Connect bulb, ammeter, variable resistor and battery in series; Connect voltmeter in parallel to bulb; Vary current using variable resistor; Use the voltmeter and ammeter to measure potential difference and current, respectively; Record at least 5 values of potential difference and current. (If possible repeat results.); Plot graph with potential difference on the x-axis and current on the y-axis.

Electrical charge and current

1 Charge flow = current × time; or $Q = I \times t$

2 **Current** is the name given to the flow of negatively **charged** particles around a closed circuit. These particles are called **electrons**. Because of their charge they are attracted to the **positive** terminal of a cell or **battery**. In books we refer to the opposite direction and call this **conventional** current flow.

3 Time = $\frac{\text{charge flow}}{\text{current}} = \frac{40}{2} = 20\,\text{s}$;

time = $\frac{\text{charge flow}}{\text{current}} = \frac{10}{2} = 5\,\text{s}$;

current = $\frac{\text{charge flow}}{\text{time}} = \frac{100}{500} = 0.2\,\text{A}$;

charge flow = current × time = 6 × 150 = 900 C

4 Time = $\frac{\text{charge flow}}{\text{current}}$; = $\frac{1800}{6} = 300\,\text{s}$,

300 s; or 5 minutes

Current, resistance and potential difference and resistors

1 a Potential difference = current × resistance or $V = I \times R$

b Ohm's law

c Constant temperature

2 Series circuit; with resistor and variable resistor; and ammeter; Voltmeter connected in parallel with fixed resistor.

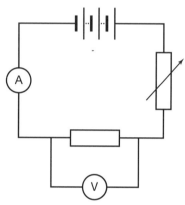

3 Vary current using variable resistor; Use the voltmeter and ammeter to measure potential difference and current respectively; Record at least 5 values of potential difference and current (If possible repeat results.); Plot graph with current on the x-axis and potential difference on the y-axis; Draw line of best fit; Calculate gradient of line to get resistance value.

4 a Thermistor

b Series circuit; with thermistor and variable resistor; and ammeter; Voltmeter connected in parallel with thermistor.

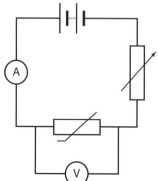

c i Thermometer; and kettle or Bunsen burner

ii 19 kΩ

iii Temperature sensor or thermostat to control central heating system

5 $R_{\text{total}} = R_1 + R_2$; = 10 + 5 = 15 Ω

6 $A_2 = 0.5\,\text{A}$, $A_3 = 1\,\text{A}$, $V_2 = 5\,\text{V}$, $V_3 = 5\,\text{V}$

Series and parallel circuits

1 In a series circuit, current is the **same** throughout the circuit and potential difference **splits** across the components. In a parallel circuit, **potential difference** is the same across each branch of the circuit and current splits through the parallel branches. An ammeter must be connected in **series** to work correctly. A voltmeter must be connected in **parallel** to work correctly.

2 a Cell in series with bulb and switch.

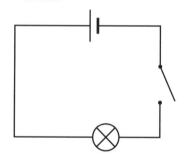

b Three bulbs in series with a battery/two cells and an ammeter connected in series.

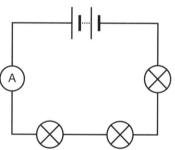

c Battery is series with bulb and thermistor. Voltmeter in parallel with thermistor.

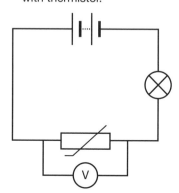

3 a Battery with two bulbs in parallel, switch correctly placed.

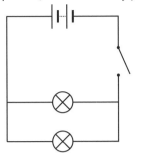

b Battery with three bulbs in parallel, switch correctly placed.

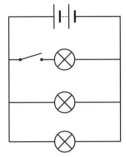

c Battery, bulb and thermistor in series bulb connected in parallel with thermistor.

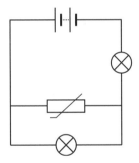

4 Idea of ring main; and parallel circuit.

Mains electricity: direct and alternating potential difference (ac/dc)

1 a dc: direct current; and ac: alternating current

b Alternating current continually changes direction and can flow in two directions; Direct current flows in one direction.

2 Transformers needed to change voltage; Transformers only work with ac; Transmission requires large potential differences to minimise current; and reduce power losses.

3 dc, 5 V (± 0.5 V)

4 10 V

Mains electricity

1 The **electricity** supplied to our homes is called **mains** electricity and it is an **alternating** current supply. This type of current

changes direction many times per second. In fact the current goes forwards and back **fifty** times per second. This means it has a **frequency** of 50 Hz.

2 a fuse; **b** live wire; **c** neutral wire; **d** earth wire.

3 a Earth wire has zero potential difference/current unless there is a fault and ensures that any metal casing is safe to touch by also being at zero pd.

b Live wire is at 230 V and provides the potential difference which makes the current flow through the appliance.

c The neutral is at 0 V this causes a potential difference between the neutral and the live wire; This causes a current to flow through the appliance.

4 a The live wire is still connected to the live terminal at 230 V and if touched the person will provide a path for charge to move to Earth; closing the circuit; A surge of current will flow through the person until the fuse melts.

b Device is double insulated; and the (plastic) casing is not a conductor.

Electric Power (with electrical devices)

1 $P = I^2 R$ or $P = IV$ or $P = \dfrac{V^2}{R}$ or $P = Et$ or other correct answer

2 $P = VI = 20 \times 2; = 40; W$

3 $P = I^2 R = 0.1^2 \times 100; = 1 W$

4 $P = \dfrac{\text{energy transferred}}{\text{time taken}}$ rearrange to:

$t = \dfrac{E}{P} = \dfrac{36\,000\,000}{10\,000} = 3600\,s$;

or 1 hour

Energy transfers in appliances

1 $E = Pt$; or $E = VIt$ (or other correct answer)

2 Everyday electrical **appliances** are designed to bring about **energy** transfers. The **amount** of energy an appliance **transfers** depends on how **long** the appliance is switched on for and the **power** of the appliance.

3 a $E = QV = 500 \times 20; = 10\,000\,J$ or 10 kJ

b $t = \dfrac{Q}{I} = \dfrac{500}{2}; = 250\,s$ or 4 minutes 10 seconds

4 a $V = IR$ rearrange to :
$R = \dfrac{V}{I} = \dfrac{12}{2} = 6;\ \Omega$

b $t = 120\,s$; $Q = It = 2 \times 120 = 240$; C

c $P = V \times I = 12 \times 2 = 24\ W$
2 minutes = 120 s
$E = P \times t = 24 \times 120 = 2880\,J$
2880 J

The National Grid

1 a 2.3 kV; **b** step-up transformer; **c** 675 kV; **d** pylon; **e** step-down transformer; **f** 230 V

2 Power is constant so if V goes up I goes down ($P = VI$); Power losses are proportional to the square of current ($P = I^2R$); Reducing the current reduces the power losses.

3 a Power losses due to comparatively high resistance of long power lines, so a lot of power is wasted on the power lines and relatively little is used to light the bulb. ($P = I^2R$).

b Student uses a step-up transformer for transmission; This increases the potential difference; and decreases the current and reduces the power losses; He uses a step-down transformer to reduce the potential difference and increase the current supplied to the bulb.

Static charge and electric fields (1)

1 a Negatively charged particles/electrons transferred by friction from the hair to the balloon; balloon becomes negatively charged.

b Hair becomes positively charged as it has lost electrons; Positively charged hair is attracted by and moves towards the negatively charged balloon; Unlike charges attract.

c Negative charges on the surface of the balloon repel negative charges in the wall; Force of attraction exists between remaining positive charges in the wall and negatively charged electrons; Unlike charges attract.

d (Water molecules are polarised so they attract charged particles.) The effect is that water is a better conductor than air and charge is able to escape the balloon.

Static charge and electric fields (2)

1 Charged, electric, friction, transferring, air, positive.

2 **a** Radial lines growing further apart; arrows pointing away from proton:

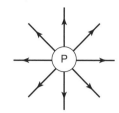

b Radial lines growing further apart; arrows pointing away from protons; lines showing repulsion effect:

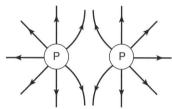

3 A lightning rod is made of a conductive material such as copper; The lightning rod is grounded or earthed; This provides a low resistance path to earth in the event of a lightning strike; The strong field around the lightning rod ensures that a lightning strike would pass through the low resistance copper generating less heat so it will not be as destructive.

Particle model

Particle model of matter and density of materials

1 The formula for density is **mass** divided by **volume** and the standard SI unit is **kg/m³**. Sometimes the values are very large so **g/cm³** are used instead. A density of **1000** kg/m³ is equal to the density of **1** g/cm³. This is also the density of water.

2 **a** Density $= \frac{mass}{volume} = \frac{56.5}{0.005}$; 11 300, kg/m³

b kg/m³ → g/cm³ = ÷1000
$\frac{11\,300}{1000} = 11.3$ g/cm³

3 Mass = density × volume
cm³ → m³ = 1 000 000 : 1 so
8000 cm³ = 0.008 m³
mass = 600 × 0.008 = 4.8 kg

4 Volume of stone = 27.5 ml – 20.0 ml = 7.5 ml; and 7.5 ml = 7.5 cm³
Density $= \frac{mass}{volume} = \frac{18}{7.5} = 2.4$ g/cm³

Changes of state and internal energy

1 A – solid; B – gas; C – liquid.
Solids: ordered, regular pattern, close together, vibration around a fixed point;

Liquids: Close together, disordered, multidirectional weaker bonds;
Gases: far apart, high speed, random motion.

2 Molecules in gases have higher average E_k than molecules in liquids; Change of state from gas (steam) to liquid (water) leads to drop in E_k of molecules; Condensation leads to steam transferring energy to glass as steam changes to water.

3 Physical

Changes of temperature and specific latent heat

1 Thermal energy change of state = mass × specific latent heat or E = mL

2 From –40°C to 0°C energy is supplied to the atoms by heating and it increases the energy in the kinetic store of the atoms, increasing temperature; During the melting stage energy continues to be supplied but there is no temperature change as the energy is being used to break the bonds as the substance changes state into a liquid; The energy store is called the latent heat of fusion; From 0°C to 100°C the energy in the kinetic store of the molecules increases; At 100°C the energy is used to break the bonds and change the water from liquid into steam; This energy store is called the latent heat of vaporisation.

3 Thermal energy change of state = mass × specific latent heat = 33.4 kJ
Thermal energy change of state = 0.1; × 334 000 J; 33400 J = 33.4 kJ

Particle motion in gases (1)

1 The molecules of gas are in constant **random** motion. The average **kinetic** energy of the **particles** is proportional to temperature on the **kelvin** scale. Changing the temperature of a gas in a container of fixed volume will change the **pressure** exerted on the sides of the **container**.

2 Random; with a range of speeds (or kinetic energies).

3 Total energy in the kinetic and potential stores; of all the particles that make up a system.

Particle motion in gases (2)

1 Pressure × volume = constant or pV = constant

2 **a** Initial temp in kelvin = K = °C + 273 = –23 °C + 273 = 250 K
Final temp = 477 °C + 273 = 750 K
Temp change = final temp – initial temp = 750 – 250 = 500 K

b Change in kinetic energy of the particles is proportional to increase in temperature on the kelvin scale; Increase from 250 to 750 is × 3 so E_k store triples

3 $p_1V_1 = p_2V_2$ so $V_2 = \frac{p_1V_1}{p_2}$;
$= \frac{120 \times 75}{225}$; = 40 cm³
(kilo prefix ignored as cancels out)

4 The work done on the gas leads to an increase in the internal energy store of the gas molecules; increasing their potential and kinetic energy stores; Subsequent increases take place in the thermal energy store of the tyre due to transfer in thermal energy stores.

Atoms

The structure of the atom (1)

1 **a** Protons; neutrons; and electrons. (in any order)

b Nucleus; protons, neutrons (protons and neutrons any order).

c Protons; electrons; neutral (protons and electrons any order).

2 Outer circle – electron; Inner circle with positive symbol – proton; Inner blank circle – neutron.

3 Row 1: 1; row 2: 0; row 3: 0, –1

4 Atoms are very small having a radius of about 1×10^{-10} m; The basic atomic structure is a positively charged nucleus; composed of both neutrons and protons orbited by negatively charged electrons; The majority of the mass of an atom is contained within the nucleus; The nucleus is very small with a nucleus less than 1/10 000 of the radius of the atom; Protons and neutrons have considerably larger masses than electrons; or The electrons are arranged at specific distances from the nucleus.

The structure of the atom (2)

1 Order p, n, e: Li = 3, 4, 3;
Be = 5, 4, 5; Cu = 29, 34, 29;
Na = 11,12,11;
K = 19, 20,19; Eu = 63, 89, 63

2 An **isotope** is an atom with the same number of **protons** and a different number of **neutrons**. **Isotopes** have the same chemical properties as the atom. If the **atomic** number is altered, the **element** changes.

3 a F

b T

c T

d F

Developing a model of the atom

1 Plum pudding is solid thereby atom is solid; Positive charge is thinly spread throughout atom (the dough); Negatively charged electrons are dotted throughout the pudding like currants.

2 Path A: A very small deflection confirms that the atom could be composed of thinly spread positive charge; This was predicted by and could be explained by the plum pudding model.

Path B: Results indicated that particularly in the case of the larger deflections that there could be a concentration of positive charge repelling positive alpha particle; This would not be predicted by the plum pudding model.

Path C: The deflections through large angles demonstrate that the atom has a concentration of positive charge and mass in a very small place; This was the first conclusive evidence for a nucleus, which was not included in the plum pudding model.

Radioactive decay and nuclear radiation

1 Some atomic nuclei are **unstable**. The nucleus emits **radiation** as it changes to become more stable. This is a **random** process called radioactive **decay**. Activity is the rate at which a source of **radioactive** nuclei decays. Activity is measured in **becquerel** (Bq).

2 Row 1: helium nuclei, mm of paper or a few cm of air; row 2: high speed electrons, medium ionising effect; row 3: a few cm of lead or metres of concrete, low ionisation effect.

3 a Alpha not penetrative enough; gamma too penetrative.

b Signal indicates thickness of paper; Feedback controls whether rollers go closer or further apart to control paper thickness.

Nuclear equations

1 $^{214}_{82}\text{Pb} \rightarrow ^{214}_{83}\text{Bi} + ^{0}_{-1}\text{e}$

2 $^{214}_{84}\text{Po} \rightarrow ^{210}_{82}\text{Pb} + ^{4}_{2}\text{He}$

3 $^{230}_{90}\text{Th} \rightarrow ^{226}_{88}\text{Ra} + ^{4}_{2}\text{He}$

Half-life of radioactive elements

1 The half-life of a radioactive isotope is the time it takes for the number of radioactive nuclei in a sample to halve; or the time it takes for the count rate (or activity) from a radioactive sample to fall to half its initial level.

2 a $1 \rightarrow \frac{1}{2} \rightarrow \frac{1}{4}$ = 2 half-lives;

$2 \times 5700 = 11\,400$ years

b $1 \rightarrow \frac{1}{2} \rightarrow \frac{1}{4} \rightarrow \frac{1}{8} \rightarrow \frac{1}{16} =$

4 half-lives; $4 \times 5700 =$ 22 800 years.

c x-axis and y-axis correctly labelled; with correct units;

First point 4000 cpm at time zero;

Plotting of 2nd, 3rd and 4th points showing 2000, 1000, 500 as count rates;

Points being plotted at times (approximately): 5700 years, 11 400 years, 17 100 and 22 800 years;

Smooth curve through plotted points.

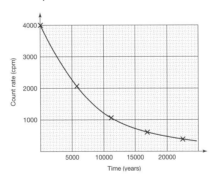

Hazards and uses of radioactive emissions (1)

1 Exposure can take place by contamination; Contamination is when the radioactive material is breathed in or ingested; Once inside the body the radiation can do damage by causing ionisation; Or irradiation; Irradiation is exposure to radiation directly; The radiation emitted can cause ionisation; Both forms can cause damage to DNA, cells and cause mutations that lead to cancer.

2 a Wearing film badges that monitor exposure; Limit exposure to as short a time as possible; Keep as far away from radioactive source as practical; This could be achieved by handling radioactive sources at arm's length (or by using tongs); Wearing protective clothing or working behind screens; Washing stations to ensure that any traces of radioactive material are removed from clothing or body to prevent later ingestion (or direct irradiation).

b It is important for the findings to be shared with other scientists; Then the findings can be checked by peer review.

3 a Radiation that is ever present emitted by man-made and natural sources.

b Atmosphere shields humans from cosmic rays; Astronauts travel above the atmosphere.

Hazards and uses of radioactive emissions (2)

1 Bismuth-214 has half-life of 20 minutes; 1 hour = 60 minutes.

Number of half-lives =

$\dfrac{\text{total time}}{\text{time per half-life}} = \dfrac{60}{20}$

= 3 (half-lives)

For 3 half-lives half 4000 3 times,

$4000 \rightarrow 2000 \rightarrow 1000 \rightarrow 500$

Count-rate 1 hour later is 500 counts/minute.

2 a To have $\frac{1}{8}$th of the original sample the sample must have undergone 3 half-lives

because $1 \rightarrow \frac{1}{2} \rightarrow \frac{1}{4} \rightarrow \frac{1}{8}$; is 3 half-lives.

b Radium-226 has a half-life of 1600 years; and $3 \times 1600 =$ 4800 years.

3 a 1 lead-210 for every 7 bismuth-210 means $\frac{1}{8}$th lead remains in sample

$1 \rightarrow \frac{1}{2} \rightarrow \frac{1}{4} \rightarrow \frac{1}{8}$ means 3 half-lives have elapsed

b $3 \times 22 = 66$ years

Hazards and uses of radioactive emissions (3)

1 Technetium-99; It emits gamma radiation that can be detected outside body; The half-life is short so as not to cause unnecessary irradiation but long enough to trace blood flow to liver.

2 **a** Xenon-133; Gamma radiation can be used in a gamma knife set-up; Individual rays do little damage due to the low ionisation of gamma, but their combined effect can destroy cells in a tumour; Gamma radiation is penetrative enough to reach the tumour.

   b Cobalt-60 can be reused several times; (As its half-life is much longer than that of xenon-133).

3 Risk of irradiation; and contamination; Chemotherapy and radiotherapy are aggressive treatments that also kill healthy cells, and can cause mutation that can also lead to cancer.

Nuclear fission and fusion

1 Fission

2 Mass number goes up by one; and atomic number remains unchanged.

3 Control rods absorb neutrons; and can slow down or stop the fission process completely; The fission rate or chain reaction can be controlled by inserting or withdrawing control rods.

4 **a** Two lighter nuclei are brought together in conditions of very high temperature and pressure; They join together to make a heavier atom and release energy in the process.

   b Similarities: Both are nuclear processes; both cause a transfer of (kinetic) energy; both release neutrons; both create different elements; both are related to $E = mc^2$; both have a mass defect.

   Differences: Fusion is the joining of small nuclei to form larger elements and fission is the splitting of large nuclei to form smaller elements; fusion occurs naturally in the Sun and fission is manufactured; fusion is safer as the waste products are not as dangerous as those of fission.

Forces

Forces and their interactions

1 Velocity

2 1– c; 2 – d; 3 – a; 4 – b

3 Direction; and magnitude/size/value.

4 **a** A contact force requires two surfaces to be touching for force to act; A non-contact force does not require surfaces to be touching for force to act.

   b Gravitational; magnetic; electrostatic, etc.

Gravity

1 Weight = mass × gravitational field strength or $W = m \times g$ and units: N or newtons.

2 Karen is correct; Mass is a measure of how much material (or how many atoms) something contains; Mass cannot be changed unless some of the material is removed; Weight is a force; A force due to an object's position in a gravitational field; Mass is measured in kg and weight is measured in N.

3 $W = mg$

   $W = 75 \times 1.6; = 120\,N$

Resultant forces

1 1 a; 3 b; 4 c; 5 e

2 **a** $3\,N \rightarrow$

   b $0\,N$

   c $6\,N \leftarrow$

3 **a** Vertical and horizontal arrow pairs should be approximately the same size, if not subtract one mark from total; Friction and air resistance can be represented as two separate arrows.

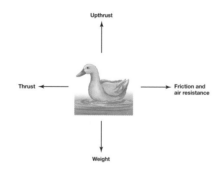

   b To accelerate there needs to be a resultant/unbalanced force; It is not possible for weight or upthrust to change; The duck needs to paddle faster to make the thrust force larger; The resultant force will now be greater than zero so the duck can accelerate.

Work done and energy transfer

1 Work done = force × distance or $W = F \times s$

2 Nm

3 **a** Work done = force × distance
   Work done = $30 \times 4; = 120; N$;

   b Work done = force × distance rearrange to
   distance = $\frac{\text{work done}}{\text{force}}$
   distance = $\frac{240}{30} = 8\,m$

   c Yes; friction between the go-kart and surface would increase the temperature of the wheels.

Forces and elasticity

1 Extension is proportional to force; provided the spring is not stretched beyond elastic limit.

2 **a** Straight line through the origin; Axes are force and extension.

   b Label force on y-axis and extension on the x-axis; then calculate gradient or reverse axes and reciprocal of gradient.

3 Inelastic deformation means the material has been permanently; stretched or squashed and will not return to its original length or shape.

Moments, levers and gears

1 A force or a **system** of forces can cause an object to **rotate**. The **turning** effect of a force is also called the **moment** of the force.

2 Nm

3 $40\,N \times 10\,m; = 50\,N \times 8\,m$;
   $400\,Nm = 400\,Nm$; So she is correct.

Pressure and pressure differences in a fluid (1)

1 Pressure = $\frac{\text{force}}{\text{area}}$

2 A liquid or a gas

3 The **pressure** in fluids causes a force **perpendicular** to any **surface**. The pressure at the surface of any fluid can be calculated using the equation **pressure = force/area**

4 Rearrange: pressure = $\frac{\text{force}}{\text{area}}$ to: force: = pressure × area;
   Force = pressure × area = $106\,000; \times 0.8 = 84\,800; N$; or $84.8\,kN$

Pressure and pressure differences in a fluid (2)

1 Pressure difference = height x density × gravitational field strength
   pressure difference = $3 \times 1000 \times 10; 30\,000; Pa$ or N/m^2

2 The air outside is now at a lower pressure than the air inside the packet.

3 Pressure in a fluid is proportional to depth; because pressure difference = height × density × gravitational field strength; Pressure exerted by water on his ears is (three times) higher at the bottom of pool, causing discomfort.

4 As water pours out of the bottle it creates a vacuum inside; Atmospheric pressure outside the bottle is higher than the pressure inside the bottle; Atmospheric pressure pushes the sides of the bottle in.

Distance, displacement, speed and velocity

1 **a** Distance

b Displacement

2 **a** Steady speed

b Acceleration

c Deceleration

3 **a** 45 m

b Distance travelled = speed × time, rearrange to

speed = $\frac{\text{distance travelled}}{\text{time}}$,

= $\frac{10}{6}$,

= 1.67 m/s

c B → C has steeper gradient/slope than A → B

4 1 – c; 2 – d; 3 – b; 4 – a

Equations of motion

1 **a** 7.1 m/s^2

b 11 m/s^2

c The cheetah's acceleration is significantly (about 60%) higher than that of the sports car. This is surprising because the car is a sports car, designed for high acceleration, and the cheetah is an animal.

2 **a** 60 s

3 **a** 3.75 m/s^2

b 4 s

Acceleration

1 **a** Acceleration

b Constant speed

c Deceleration

2 **a** Acceleration = $\frac{\text{change in velocity}}{\text{time taken}}$
= $\frac{10}{10}$ = 1; m/s^2

b Acceleration = $\frac{\text{change in velocity}}{\text{time taken}}$

Acceleration = $\frac{15-10}{30-10}$
= 0.25 m/s^2

c Steady or constant speed

3 Triangle area = 0.5 × b × h
rectangle area = b × h

triangles: 0.5 × 10 × 10 = 50 m
and 0.5 × 5 × 20 = 50 m

rectangle: 10 × 20 = 200

Total distance = 50 + 50 + 200
= 300 m

Newton's laws of motion

1 The **velocity** of an object will only change if there is a **resultant** force acting on it. When a car is at a **steady** speed the driving force and **resistive** forces of friction and **drag** are equal and act in **opposite** directions.

2 The acceleration of an object is proportional; to the resultant force acting on the object the object; and inversely proportional to the mass of the object; F = ma.

3 Measure of how difficult it is to change an object's motion.

4 **a** Arrow is equal and opposite.

b The force exerted by the boy on the boat; is the same magnitude as the force exerted by the boat on the boy.

c This is an example of Newton's third law.

5 **a** 15 – 10 = 5 N

b → or 'right'

c Resultant force = mass × acceleration rearrangement:
acceleration = $\frac{\text{resultant force}}{\text{mass}}$
acceleration = $\frac{5}{100}$ = 0.05 m/s^2

6 **a** Zero

b Resultant force = mass × acceleration: rearrangement:
acceleration = $\frac{\text{resultant force}}{\text{mass}}$
acceleration = $\frac{8000}{800}$; = 10 m/s^2

c Acceleration = $\frac{\text{change in velocity}}{\text{time taken}}$

rearrangement:

time taken = $\frac{\text{change in velocity}}{\text{acceleration}}$

time taken = $\frac{30}{10}$; = 3 s

Stopping distance

1 Thinking distance; + braking distance

2 **a** Condition of brakes; tyres; and condition of road surface (wet, icy, etc.).

b **i** Thinking distance is proportional to speed.

ii Braking distance increases more and more with each increase in speed; Braking distance is not proportional to speed but to the square of speed.

3 One of the students could be looking at a mobile phone; A second student could drop the ruler without warning between his fingers; They could check how far the ruler falls through the finger to indicate reaction time; The further the ruler falls the longer the reaction time; The test could be repeated several times (possibly with other students); They could then compare the results with the mobile phone to those results taken without a mobile phone.

Momentum (1)

1 kg m/s

2 Momentum = mass × velocity or p = m × v

3 p = mv; = 1000 × 400
= 400 000; kg m/s

4 p = mv; = 3.5; × 10 = 35; kg m/s

Momentum (2)

1 In a **closed** system (in which no **external** forces act) the total momentum before an event is equal to the total momentum after the event. This is called the **conservation** of **momentum** law.

2 **a** p = mv = 2000 × 40 = 80 000; kg m/s

b Momentum = combined mass × velocity
combined mass of car and truck = 2000 + 800 = 2800 kg
velocity = $\frac{\text{momentum}}{\text{combined mass}}$;
= $\frac{80\,000}{2800}$ = 28.6 m/s

3 Momentum of car 1: p = mv
= 800 × 40 = 32 000; kg m/s
(momentum direction →)
Momentum of car 2: p = mv
= 1000 × 30 = 30 000; kg m/s
(momentum direction ←)
Combined mass of car 1 and 2
= 800 kg + 1000 kg = 1800 kg
Final momentum = momentum of car 1 – momentum of car 2
= 32 000 – 30 000 = 2000; kg m/s
Velocity = $\frac{\text{momentum}}{\text{combined mass}}$ = $\frac{2000}{1800}$
= 1.1 m/s →

Momentum (3)

1 The car is made of material that is not too hard, so it will crumple in a collision; Force felt by occupants in a collision is $F = \frac{m\Delta v}{\Delta t}$ (expressed as formula or words); Crumple zones effectively make the time of the collision longer; If time is made longer; force experienced by occupants is made smaller; The force can be reduced to a level that will result in a less serious/non-fatal injury.

2 $F = \frac{m\Delta v}{\Delta t}$ rearrangement required: change in momentum = $F\Delta t$

change in momentum = $180 \times 0.005 = 0.9$; Ns or kg m/s

3 a Change in momentum = $F\Delta$
= $200 \times 0.005 = 1$; Ns or kg m/s

   b $\frac{m\Delta v}{\Delta t}$ rearrangement required:
$\Delta v = \frac{F\Delta t}{m}$
= $\Delta v = \frac{200 \times 0.005}{0.050} = 20$ m/s

Waves

Transverse and longitudinal waves

1 Transverse

2 a Vibrations of molecules or particles are parallel; to direction of wave motion/energy transfer.

   b Sound waves, P-waves, any other correct response.

   c Wave fronts closer together; and wave fronts further apart:

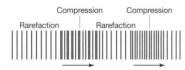

Compression   Compression
Rarefaction   Rarefaction

3 a Transverse; because vibrations are at right angles; to direction of wave motion/energy transfer.

   b Instead of up and down push it in and out; so that vibrations are same direction as wave motion.

   c In longitudinal waves particles vibrate parallel to wave motion/energy transfer; whereas in transverse waves vibrations are at right angles (to wave motion/energy transfer).

Properties of waves

1 a The distance from the rest position/mid-point/equilibrium/undisturbed position; to the maximum displacement of a wave.

   b The number of vibrations; per second; (of a wave) or number of waves passing a point per second.

   c The distance from a point on the wave; to the equivalent point on the adjacent wave.

2 a 4 ms

   b Frequency $= \frac{1}{\text{time period}} = \frac{1}{0.004}$
= 250 Hz

   c 3 squares and each 1 cm square = 1V;
$3 \times 1V = 3V$

3 $v = f \times \lambda$ rearrangement required:
$\lambda = v/f$; $= \frac{300\,000\,000}{603\,000} = 497.5$; m

Reflection and refraction

1 Absorption; reflection; transmission (accept refraction also).

2 Angle reflected wave makes with incident ray should be 90°; Reflected ray should be horizontal and have an arrow showing direction; Wave fronts should be perpendicular to horizontal reflected ray.

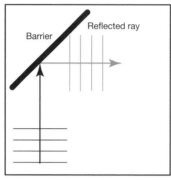

Barrier   Reflected ray

After reflection

3 a Ray inside block refracted towards normal in glass; Ray leaving the block must be refracted away from the normal; Angle ray makes with normal leaving block must be very close to angle ray made with normal before entering the block. (Rays must be labelled with an arrow and drawn with a ruler.)

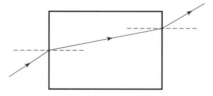

   b Ray bends towards the normal when entering the block; Ray bends away from the normal when leaving the block; Ray leaving the block and entering the block are both horizontal. (Rays must be labelled with an arrow and drawn with a ruler).

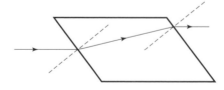

Sound waves (1)

1 20 Hz; to 20 000 Hz (or 20 kHz)

2 Air molecules are compressed or pushed together by speaker; Air molecules spread out or rarefaction takes place; Sound waves are collected by outer ear and channeled into inner ear; Ear drum vibrates; Small bones (ossicles) in ear vibrate; at same frequency as original sound; Fluid in cochlea vibrates; Auditory nerve converts vibrations to electrical impulses sent to brain.

3 a 7 squares and each square = 1 ms $1 \times 7 = 7$ ms

   b Frequency $= \frac{1}{\text{time period}} = \frac{1}{0.007}$;
$f = 143$ Hz

   c 4 squares and each square = 1V;
$4 \times 1V = 4V$

Sound waves (2)

1 Sound above; 20 kHz (or accept above human hearing range).

2 Medical imaging, destroying gall or kidney stones, industrial imaging or other correct response.

3 a A P-wave is a primary wave/It is the first wave to arrive in an earthquake; It is a longitudinal wave. A longitudinal wave is one where the vibrations of the wave are parallel to; its motion.

   b An S-wave is a secondary wave/It the second wave to arrive in an earthquake; It is a transverse wave. A transverse wave is one where the vibrations of the wave are perpendicular/at right angles/at 90 degrees; to its motion.

   c Density of the rock changes; so speed changes; Density changes gradually, so the paths are curved; This is a refraction effect.

   d The core is liquid; and only P-waves can travel through liquids.

Electromagnetic waves (1)

1 a Long

   b Short

   c Low

   d High

   e infrared

   f ultraviolet

2 Transverse; travel through a vacuum/space; all travel at the speed of light through a vacuum (accept other sensible responses).

3 Radiowaves have longer wavelengths than microwaves; Radiowaves can be reflected by the ionosphere; The ionosphere is an ionised/charged layer of the upper atmosphere; Radiowaves can be transmitted to points where receiver is not in line of sight; Radiowaves can be transmitted with this method around the globe; Microwaves have shorter wavelengths and can pass through the Earth's atmosphere; Microwaves can be used to

transmit information to and from satellites in orbit; Microwaves need to be transmitted to points where the receiver is in the line of site; Microwaves can be used for telephone, television and internet.

Electromagnetic waves (2)

1 Radio waves

2 The type of radiation; and the size of the dose.

3 1– b; 2 – f; 3 – c; 4 – a; 5 – d; 6 – e.

Lenses

1 **a** Convex/converging; Concave/diverging

   b Real and virtual

2 **a** Parallel lines correctly labelled and middle line continues horizontally; Focal length and principal focus correctly labelled; Labelled convex and top and bottom rays converging as per diagram.

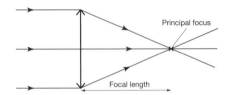

   b Parallel lines correctly labelled and middle line continues horizontally; Focal length and principal focus correctly labelled; Virtual lines passing through principal focus as dotted lines on the left side of lens; Lines then continued as continuous lines on the right side of the lens (light rays must be drawn with a ruler).

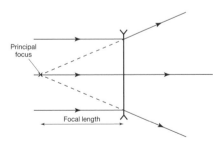

3 **a** Horizontal line from object to lens; line from top of lens passing through focal point; distance to image must be 8 cm +/− 10%; line from top of object through centre of lens to intersection point; intersect of at least two lines; image drawn with arrow. (Allow the construction lines through focal point on object side and parallel line to principal axis).

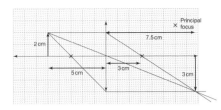

   b Real, enlarged and inverted (upside down).

   c Magnification = $\frac{\text{image height}}{\text{object height}}$

   $= \frac{3}{2.0}$; $= x$; $\times 1.5 \pm 10\%$

Visible light

1 **a** Specular

   b Diffuse (or scattering)

2 **a** Translucent; transparent.

   b Absorption; transmission; and reflection.

   c Opaque

3 **i** red, green and blue (in any order).

   ii red and blue (answer must be consistent with choices in part i).

   iii red

   iv red

Emission and absorption of infrared radiation and black body radiation

1 It is constant.

2 The black can is a better emitter of radiation than the white can; The black can is able to radiate more infrared radiation than the white can (in the 15 minutes); The temperature drop is less for the white can as it radiates away less infrared radiation.

3 **a** Both of the cans will increase in temperature; The black can will increase to a higher temperature; because black is a better absorber of infrared radiation than white.

   b In both cans the absorption of infrared will not be the only factor that affects temperature, both cans will increase their thermal store via conduction; Also the dissipation will take place (from the can) to the thermal store of the surroundings and table due to conduction and convection; When the water has evaporated the results will become meaningless.

4 Absorption of infrared is greater than emission of infrared.

5 **a** The wavelength at which the greatest intensity of radiation is emitted.

   b As temperature increases; the peak wavelength decreases.

6 The Earth absorbs infrared radiation from the Sun, this increases the temperature of the Earth; The Earth then radiates infrared (IR) back into space. This decreases the Earth's temperature; The Earth radiates IR back into space that is a lower frequency that the IR from the Sun (the Sun has a higher temperature than the Earth); The IR radiation emitted by the Earth is absorbed by greenhouse gases such as methane or carbon dioxide; The greenhouse gases re-radiate this IR in all directions but some of the IR goes back to Earth; The atmosphere acts as an 'insulating-layer', preventing the Earth from depleting its thermal store during the night; The correct amount of greenhouse gases maintains the correct temperature and prevents it getting too cold; Too many greenhouse gases would lead to an increase in temperature.

Electromagnetism

Magnetism

1 The magnetic fields are the strongest.

2 **a** An object that becomes a magnet; when placed in a magnetic field.

   b Attractive

   c Take a known magnet and push the north pole at one end of the material; Push the same north pole towards the other end of the material; If attraction always takes place, the object is an induced magnet. If both repulsion and attraction take place in the above test, the object is a permanent magnet.

3 **a**

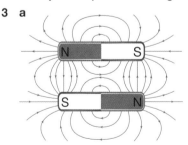

   b

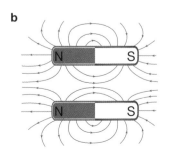

Answers

Electromagnetism

1. **a** The needle will deflect in one direction; and then go back to the centre position.

    b The needle will deflect in the opposite direction; and then go back to the centre position.

2. At least 3 concentric rings; distance between rings increases the further out you go; arrow direction of magnetic field lines anti-clockwise.

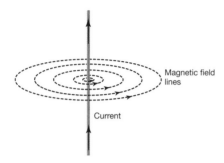

At least 3 concentric rings; distance between rings increases the further out you go; arrow direction of magnetic field lines clockwise.

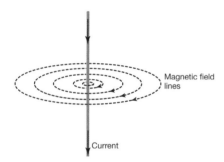

3. **a** Arrow out of the page

    b Motor effect

    c Magnet with greater field strength; larger current; wire in a coil.

Motor effect

1. **a** split-ring commutator; **b** force; **c** rotating coil; **d** force; **e** brush; **f** dc power supply.

2. **a** Current direction changes every half turn; to keep the coil spinning in the same direction.

    b The brushes connect the wire to a power supply; and make contact with the split-ring commutator.

3. The MP3 player converts the sounds into an alternating current to the solenoid; The current in the solenoid induces a magnetic field; The solenoid magnetic field is constantly changing; The solenoid is repelled and attracted by the permanent magnet; The solenoid is attached to the paper cone; As the solenoid moves back and forth it makes the paper cone vibrate producing sound waves; The compressions and rarefactions of the sound waves produced match the frequency and amplitude of the original recording.

Electromagnetic induction

1. **a** F
    b F
    c T
    d T

2. **a** Needle deflects to one side of the galvanometer; then returns to zero deflection.

    b Generator effect; If a conductor moves at right angles to a magnetic field; when the conductor cuts through the flux lines; a potential difference is induced across the ends of the conductor; If there is a complete circuit a current is also induced in the conductor.

    c The needle will deflect in the opposite direction; then return to zero deflection.

    d The needle will rock from side to side; The student will be generating an ac voltage; The frequency of the output voltage/current will match the frequency of the vibrations.

3. **a** A magnet rotates near a coil of wire; The coil is cutting through the changing field/flux lines of the magnet; An alternating potential difference is induced in the coil; The circuit is complete so the bulb is supplied with an alternating current.

    b If you go very slowly or stop completely you will no longer have a light on; This is obviously very dangerous and could impair your visibility to other road users.

Transformers

1. **a** The circuit contains a battery which supplies a current to the circuit; If somebody talks into the microphone its resistance changes; If the resistance goes down the current goes up, and vice versa.

    b The coil wrapped around the permanent magnet is a solenoid; If it is supplied with a changing current then the solenoid's magnetic field changes with it; This means that the solenoid will be repelled or attracted by different amounts by the permanent magnet; This changing attraction/repulsion makes the metal plate vibrate.

    c The coil needs to be wrapped onto a magnet, otherwise it would not be repelled; or attracted, and would not vibrate the metal disk.

2. Step-up transformer; because it has more coils on the secondary than on the primary coil.

3. **a** A changing potential difference in the primary coil induces a changing magnetic field in the core; The changing magnetic field in the core means that flux lines are constantly being cut by the secondary coil; A changing potential difference is induced in the secondary coil; The size and direction of this potential difference change as the voltage applied to the primary coil changes; If there is a complete circuit an alternating current will flow in the secondary coil.

    b A transformer will only work with ac supply as without a changing magnetic field in the core no potential difference can be induced in the secondary coil.

    For a transformer to work a changing magnetic field must be induced in the core; to induce an alternating potential difference in the secondary coil; A constant dc voltage will not induce a changing magnetic field in the core.

Space physics

Our solar system

1. The Milky Way

2. **a** Venus; Mars; Saturn; Neptune.

    b Pluto has been reclassified; as a dwarf/minor planet.

    c Moon

    d The Sun

3. Dwarf Planet – 2; Planet – 3; Sun – 4; Solar System – 5; Galaxy – 6; Universe – 7.

Life cycle of a star

1. When a star is a main sequence star, this means the inward force of **gravity** is balanced with the outward radiation pressure

caused by **fusion**. This state of **equilibrium** can last for millions to billions of years depending on the star's **mass**. When a star similar in size to our own runs out of **hydrogen** it grows in size and becomes a **red giant**.

2

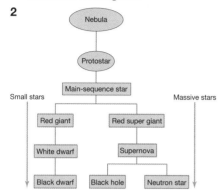

3   Most of the early Universe was hydrogen and a smaller amount of helium; The Sun and other stars use fusion to release energy; Hydrogen nuclei fuse to form helium and heavier elements; Fusion reactions can make elements up to iron; Heavier

elements are formed when a star larger than ours collapses and there is a supernova; A supernova casts matter into the Universe.

Orbital motion, natural and artificial satellites

1   Gravity

2   Similarities: both are objects that orbit another object; that is larger or has a larger mass.

Differences: artificial satellites have been launched by people into orbit; whereas a natural satellite is one that is already orbiting a planet and people did not put it there.

3   a   The time it takes the comet to make one orbit of the Sun.

    b   Speed increases due to an increase in the gravitational field strength when the comet is closer to the Sun.

4   Direction is constantly changing;, so velocity is also changing; Acceleration is change in velocity per unit of time, so acceleration is taking place.

5   a   It is not constant (or it is changing).

    b   It will change as the forces on it change; Speed will be greatest when the force of gravity is greatest or when object is closest to the Sun.

Red-shift

1   a   The Universe started from a very small region (a singularity); that was very hot and dense.

    b   Observations of supernovae.

2   a   The light from the distant galaxy; has been shifted to the red end (longer wavelength) of the spectrum.

    b   The galaxy is accelerating away from us; and the acceleration is greater than the nearby galaxy.

    c   The red-shift observation supports the idea that the Universe is expanding and the rate of expansion is increasing.

3   a   Dark energy

    b   Dark matter